Contents

HEY THERE PEOPLE OF EARTH! ARE YOU READY FOR THE BEST ANNUAL IN THE WHOLE WORLD? NOW'S YOUR CHANCE TO RELIVE TOP EPISODES FROM iCARLY, PIT YOUR WITS ON COOL PUZZLES, READ THE CAST'S LATEST BLOGS AND FIND OUT WHAT IT'S REALLY LIKE WORKING ON A WEBSHOW. SO WHAT YOU WAITING FOR? TIME TO TURN THE PAGE...

Pedigree®

Published 2009 by Pedigree Books Limited, Beech Hill House,
Walnut Gardens, Exeter, Devon, EX4 4DH.
Web: www.pedigreebooks.com • Email: books@pedigreegroup.co.uk

This iCarly Annual
2010 belongs to

_____

£7.99

Log on!

Draw a cool portrait of yourself in here.

NAME:

USER NAME:

BIRTHDAY:

STAR SIGN:

HAIR COLOUR:

EYE COLOUR:

HOMETOWN:

FAVOURITE FOOD:

REC ●

SO THIS IS ME!

Congratulations! You've decided to search for iCarly
– the coolest destination on the web! Before we get started,
input some info about yourself. If you're gonna join the
team, we want to know EVERYTHING that makes you tick!

Go

FAVOURITE THINGS TO DO
(APART FROM WATCHING iCARLY 24/7!):

DISLIKES:

MOST LIKELY TO SAY:

LEAST LIKELY TO SAY:

THE iCARLY FILES

FAVOURITE iCARLY EPISODE:

TOP CHARACTER:

THE CLIP I'D SEND
IN TO iCARLY:

CARLY

Favourite food:
Spencer's spaghetti tacos (recipe might sound a bit wacky, but wait til you try 'em!)

Name: Carly Shay

Birthday: January 14

Star sign: Capricorn

Hair colour: Dark brown

Eye colour: Brown

Hometown: Seattle

Favourite things to do:
iCarly!!! Listen to music, hang with friends, and watch movies

Dislikes:
Homework, uncool adults, being sticky, Sam and Freddie fighting too much, BUGS!!!

Most likely to say:
Contact us at iCarly.com!

Least likely to say:
Fancy a smoothie Nevel?

CARLY CLICK TEST

Think you know what makes Carly tick? Read the questions then, colour in the cursor that points to the right answer.

1. Carly's favourite teacher is Miss Briggs.

   True   False

2. Carly's parents are in the military.

   True   False

3. Carly is in the 6th grade at school.

   True   False

4. When the show got started, Carly threw a crazy hat party.

   True   False

5. Carly's always getting into trouble with Principal Franklin.

   True   False

sam

Favourite things to do:
Sit on Carly's couch,
torment Freddie,
slurp smoothies

Name: Sam Puckett

Birthday: April 17

Star sign: Aries

Hair colour: Blonde

Eye colour: Blue

Hometown: Seattle

Favourite food:
I'll eat anything that
doesn't eat me first!
Cereal and root beer is
a pretty cool breakfast.

Dislikes:
Freddie (sometimes),
school (except for lunch),
homework, celery, effort

Least likely to say:
Which way for extra
maths coaching?

Most likely to say:
I need some ham!

SAM CLICK TEST

Good luck, Sam's a tough nut to crack! Colour each of the cursors that point to the correct answers.

1. Sam lives in Carly's apartment block.

   True   False

2. Although she's always in trouble, she does try and do her best.

   True   False

3. Sam's first kiss was with Freddie.

   True   False

4. Sam is the tech-producer of iCarly.

   True   False

5. Sam's mum is called Mrs Benson.

   True    False

11

freddie

Dislikes:
Sam's big mouth, Sam's big fists, being treated like I'm still at kindergarten by my mum.

Name:	Freddie Benson
Birthday:	February 4
Star sign:	Aquarius
Hair colour:	Brown
Eye colour:	Brown
Hometown:	Seattle

Favourite food:
Popcorn, juicy watermelon, my mum's chicken soup

Favourite things to do:
Hangin' with Carly, doing iCarly, tech stuff, playing on my Pearbook computer

Most likely to say:
You guys are making me nervous!

Least likely to say:
Can my mum come too?

FREDDIE CLICK TEST

Can you pick Freddie fact from Freddie fiction? Colour in the cursor that points to the right answer each time.

1. Freddie is captain of the school AV Club.

True   False

2. It was Freddie that uploaded the first clip of Sam and Carly onto the net.

True   False

3. Freddie has a pet turtle called Monty.

True   False

4. As well as tech stuff, Freddie's totally into football.

True   False

5. Freddie's first date was with a girl called Valerie.

True   False

SPENCER

Name: Spencer Shay

Birthday: November 11

Star sign: Scorpio

Hair colour: Brown

Eye colour: Brown

Hometown: Seattle

Favourite things to do:
Making sculptures,
wearing AWESOME socks,
hangin' with my bud
Socko, putting glue on my
fingers then peeling it off

Dislikes:
Wearing suits, filling
in forms, anything that
involves sitting at a desk
and being sensible

Least likely to say:
Let me just check
my schedule!

Most likely to say:
Who says I'm abnormal?

SPENCER CLICK TEST

Have you got Spencer sussed?
Choose the right cursor outline and
then... you know what to do!

1. Spencer attended law
school for three days.

True   False

2. Spencer's buddy Socko sells ties.

True   False

3. Spencer's sculptures have
won world records.

True   False

4. Spencer is twenty-nine years old.

True   False

5. Spencer always wanted
to be an artist.

True   False

CARLY AND SAM GET SOME OF THEIR BEST MATERIAL FROM THE LOVABLE BUNCH OF CRACKPOTS THAT THEY COME ACROSS EVERY DAY! HERE'S THE LOWDOWN ON SOME OF THE CRANKIEST...

LEWBERT

It would be great if there was something nice to say about Lewbert, but there truly isn't! Lewbert is the doorman of Bushwell Plaza, Carly's apartment block. He's a cantankerous character who totally HATES kids! He also has a gross wart on his cheek that he really should do something about.

MRS BENSON

Freddie's mum is over-protective, pushy and a constant source of EMBARRASSMENT! Her precious boy can't leave the house without flossing twice, brushing and changing his socks. Mrs Benson thinks that Spencer is too immature to be looking after Carly, but sometimes she picks his brains in an attempt to find out what kids are doing these days.

iSPY CLICK TEST

Are you totally up on Carly's world? Tick the click that sounds right each time, working your way from **Lewbert** through to **Nevel Papperman**.

1. Lewbert thinks that Freddie's mum is a hottie!

   True   False

2. Mrs Benson loves Lewbert too.

   True   False

3. Miss Briggs' Christian name is Tabitha.

   True   False

4. Principal Franklin is allergic to chewing gum.

   True   False

5. Nevel's favourite phrase is 'you'll rue the day!'.

   True   False

PRINCIPAL FRANKLIN ▼

Ridgeway's headteacher is an easy going principal who genuinely cares about every pupil in his school. He sees Sam regularly in a bid to keep up-to-date with her latest bouts of troublemaking. Generally Principal Franklin's punishments are firm but fair.

NEVEL PAPPERMAN ▼

Nevel is the ingenious eleven-year-old who writes nevelocity.com – a blog spot that reviews the best and worst on the web. As well as being a fully-accredited DWEEB, Nevel is mean, cold-hearted and breathtakingly DEVIOUS! The little upstart has a crush on Carly, worse luck for her!

MISS BRIGGS ▼

The very sound of this name sends most kids at Ridgeway Junior High into a cold sweat. Miss Briggs is an old-fashioned English teacher who seems to deliberately set out to make each of her classes as B-O-R-I-N-G as possible. She is constantly barging into the Principal's office to complain about Sam Puckett's behaviour.

Best Friends FLOWCHART »»»

EVEN THOUGH THEY'RE SWORN BFF, CARLY AND SAM ARE LIKE CHALK AND CHEESE! WHICH HALF OF iCARLY'S DYNAMIC DUO IS THE MOST LIKE YOU? PLACE YOUR FINGER AT THE START OF THE FLOWCHART, THEN ANSWER YES OR NO TO EACH OF THE QUESTIONS UNTIL YOU DISCOVER WHICH WEBSTAR'S PERSONALITY IS CLOSEST TO YOURS.

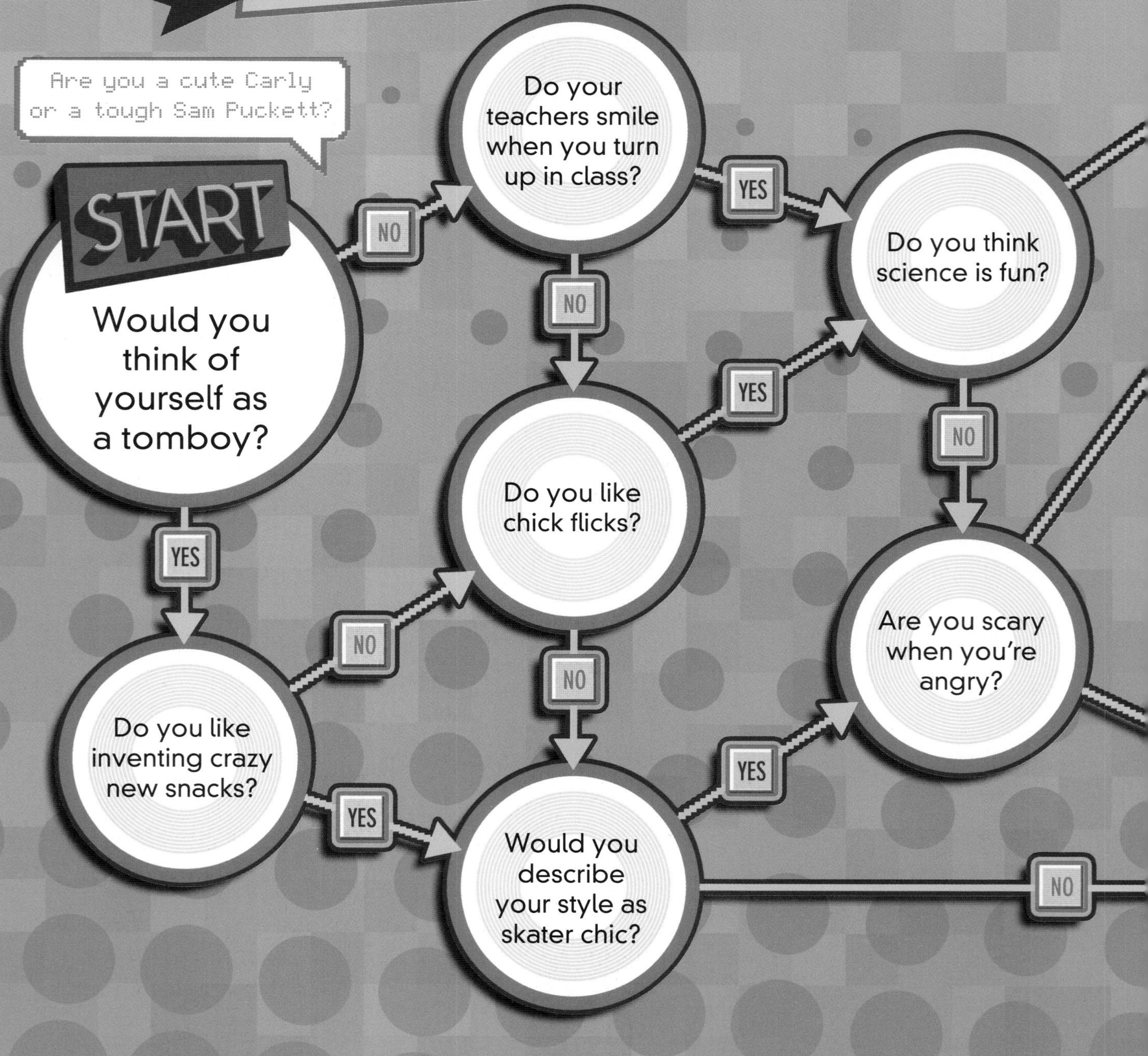

Are you a cute Carly or a tough Sam Puckett?

START

Would you think of yourself as a tomboy?

Do your teachers smile when you turn up in class?

NO

YES

Do you think science is fun?

NO

NO

YES

Do you like chick flicks?

YES

NO

Do you like inventing crazy new snacks?

NO

Are you scary when you're angry?

YES

Would you describe your style as skater chic?

YES

NO

YES

Is watching trash TV your ultimate night in?

YES

NO

NO

NO

You're kind, thoughtful and hard-working, just like Carly!

Are you good at standing up for yourself?

YES

NO

You're feisty, rebellious and fun - howdy Sam #2!

YES

Is sleep more important than schoolwork?

YES

Splashface CRASH!

FREDDIE'S BEEN TRYING TO UPDATE THE iCARLY SERVER, BUT HE HAS HIT THE WRONG KEY! NOW SPLASHFACE HAS CORRUPTED AND ALL THE FIGURES ON THE SCREEN HAVE BEEN BLACKED OUT. STUDY THE OUTLINES AND SEE IF YOU CAN WORK OUT WHO IS WHO.

REC

Ridgeway WORDSEARCH

- ☑ MISS BRIGGS
- ☑ DOUBLE MATHS
- ☑ LOCKER GOSSIP
- ☑ DRAMA
- ☑ SCIENCE
- ☑ HOMEWORK
- ☑ REPORTS
- ☑ MR DEVLIN
- ☑ ASSEMBLY
- ☑ LUNCH

L	O	C	K	E	R	G	O	S	S	I	P
S	Y	L	L	U	I	B	N	E	C	P	S
S	G	T	S	A	Q	E	N	L	I	J	H
H	Q	G	Z	M	V	S	Y	H	E	R	T
O	P	D	I	A	T	Z	L	M	N	F	A
M	B	S	Y	R	S	Z	B	I	C	D	M
E	D	Y	O	D	B	V	M	O	E	S	E
W	B	P	K	P	H	S	E	S	W	U	L
O	E	W	X	N	C	F	S	D	R	K	B
R	E	H	A	P	N	J	S	I	F	D	U
K	R	F	J	J	U	S	A	W	M	G	O
M	R	D	E	V	L	I	N	E	H	U	D

EVEN INTERNATIONAL WEBSTARS HAVE TO GO TO SCHOOL. BEING A STUDENT AT RIDGEWAY JUNIOR HIGH HAS ITS UPS AND DOWNS, WITH MISS BRIGG'S MONDAY MORNING ENGLISH CLASS SITTING FIRMLY AT ROCK BOTTOM!

Draw a line through all the good and bad aspects of Ridgeway in the grid below. The ten words could be running horizontally, vertically, diagonally or even back to front!

iWanna Stay With Spencer

Carly always knew her brother was a little unusual, but what did that matter?

 **HEY!** Carly flashed a grin at the camera. "Welcome to this week's show!"

Sam cut in and introduced herself, while Freddie tracked her on his camcorder. This episode of iCarly was looking sooo awesome! The theme of the week was action movies. "Guess what?" beamed Sam. "We love watching dudes fight." Carly squared up to her co-host then bared her fists. "We know the punches aren't really real though."
POW!

Carly ducked left and right, before delivering a knock out punch to Sam's cheek! Her friend swooned dramatically to the floor. Yep – TV certainly was a powerful medium.
"Looked like I punched her, right?" grinned Carly.
Suddenly Sam popped up again, scarlet liquid oozing out of her nose. She seemed dazed. Carly's face fell. "Oh my god, are you alright?"

"I-I think so," stuttered Sam, before breaking into a cheesy grin. "'Cos they use fake blood!"
"Now let's see some video clips," giggled Carly. Today the iCarly team had planned a great interview to finish off the webcast – Spencer was coming into the studio! "Now my brother is gonna show you his latest masterpiece," beamed Carly.

Sam hit the applause button hooked onto her belt. "Here's Spencer!" Spencer was a natural. After he had made his big entrance, the artist pulled a sheet off a huge sculpture in the corner of the set. "I was watching a building show on TV when I got inspired to create this," explained Spencer. "It's a fan of hammers!" The sculpture looked like a giant fan, but the coolest thing about it was that the blades were made of hammers!
"It actually works!" cheered Sam.
Spencer yanked a cord underneath the fan and the hammers began to spin. Everything was great 'til smoke started coming out the side. The hammers got faster and faster, whizzing out of control. "Hit the floor!" yelled Spencer. It was a lifesaving call. Milliseconds after Carly had ducked a hammer flew off the fan, digging itself into the wall just above her head.

The next night, Carly and her friends were hanging out at the apartment when there was a knock at the door. "If it's Freddie's mum," warned Sam. "Don't let her in." Spencer peeped through the spyglass to check that they were safe from Mrs Benson. "Grandad!" he gasped instead, opening the door. Carly hopped off the couch and ran over to give her grandfather a cuddle. "How's my little gumdrop?" beamed Mr Shay.

Spencer looked suspicious. "Why didn't ya tell us you were coming?" "What?" asked his grandad, a little defensively. "Can't a man drive 90 minutes to surprise his favourite grandkids?" While the Shay family shared a three-way hug, Sam nudged Freddie in the ribs. "How come my grandfather just sleeps and burps?" she wondered.

Freddie knew exactly why. "Because he's related to you!" Carly excitedly pulled her grandfather into the room. "You remember Freddie?" "Course," smiled Mr Shay. "He lives across the hall." "And I think you met Sam last time you were here," added Carly. Mr Shay's smile dropped a touch. "She borrowed ten dollars from me then ate my sandwich." Sam looked up from the couch and waved proudly. Mr Shay rummaged in his pocket, then pulled out a gift card for the Groovy Smoothies café across the street. "I got a present for you," he explained, passing the card to Carly. "Thirty bucks!" grinned Sam. "Let's go and spend that bad boy!" Carly shook her head. "My Grandad only just got here." Mr Shay didn't seem to mind. "Go have some fun! I'm in town for a few days." Chuffed, the kids grabbed their jackets and headed for the door. "Bring me back a Blueberry Banana Blitz," hollered Spencer. "See ya whenever."

iWanna Stay With Spencer

AS soon as the door had clicked shut behind Carly, Mr Shay's mood changed completely. "Are you outta your mind?" he roared, as Spencer agonised over his favourite smoothie flavours. "Should I have gone for the Strawberry Splat?" asked Spencer.

Mr Shay reminded his grandson of the latest edition of iCarly. In an attempt to get down with the kids it seemed that he'd logged on and watched the full horror of the fan of hammers stunt! "You nearly took Carly's head off!" shouted Mr Shay. "It was incredibly irresponsible." Spencer straightened up. "I am responsible. It was an accident."

"You think it's OK for a responsible guardian to tell a thirteen-year-old that she can just come home 'whenever'?" demanded his grandad. "She's across the street with two friends!" bellowed Spencer. "She has a cell phone with her all the time." Mr Shay was already pacing the floor, shaking his head in disappointment. "I wish you hadn't dropped out of law school to become an artist." Spencer could see it was going to be a long night. They had been through the law school thing a thousand times already over the years. When would Mr Shay senior understand that being a lawyer was the last thing he wanted to do?

"Lawyers can't do this!" he yelled, pulling up his shirt and rubbing his stomach like a loony. "You had such a bright future," sighed Mr Shay wistfully. Spencer gave up. He stuck his earplugs in, then turned his MP3 up to full volume. "I'm sorry," he shrugged. "I can't hear you. I'm rocking out!" While he did his best to ignore him, grandad followed his grandson round the room. It wasn't 'til he said that Carly had to come and live with him that Spencer pulled out the plugs. "I love you Spencer," explained Mr Shay. "But Carly needs a responsible adult authority figure in her life."

"Hey Spence!" called Carly sticking her head round the front door an hour later. "I'm back with one large Blueberry Banana Blitz!" Spencer stopped pacing back and forwards in front of the TV. "Where have you been?" he demanded. "At the Groovy Smoothie?" replied Carly. She hadn't seen her bro so agitated since he lost one of his glow-in-the-dark socks.

"No excuses," snapped Spencer, trying to be super-stern. "You're out of control."

"Are you on some sort of medication I should know about?" asked Carly. Spencer grimaced. "When you live under my roof, you live by my rules. Er… and always try your best and eat your vegetables!" It was the longest lecture he had ever delivered. Afterwards Spencer felt totally drained. "I can't do this," he yelped, dropping the strict father act. Carly started to worry. "Do what?"

"After you left, grandad said he didn't think that I was responsible enough to take care of you," groaned Spencer. "That's insane!" said Carly. After all, she was responsible enough for both of them, wasn't she? Spencer continued. "He thinks you'd be better off living with him in Yakima." Carly's mind whirled. Yakima, YAKIMA, for goodness sake?! She couldn't think of anywhere she's rather not be. "We're just going to have to change grandad's mind," she decided. "I am not moving to Yakima."

Spencer nodded his head. "Don't worry too much about this," he agreed. "Just go do your homework or something." Carly grabbed her backpack and headed for the stairs. "I mean," rephrased Spencer, putting on his 'authority' voice. "You go do your homework right now, young lady!" Carly gave him a salute and tripped up the stairs to her bedroom. "Yes sir!" If they made a superhuman effort, they could do 'responsible' for sure.

iWanna Stay With Spencer

THE next night, Carly was too nervy to sit down and relax with Freddie and Sam. While her friends hung out in the studio, she paced back and forwards trying to come up with reasons why she shouldn't move in with her grandad.

"Will you please chill?" said Sam. All this pacing was interrupting her rest time.

"I'll chill when Spencer's persuaded my grandad that he's a responsible adult!" snapped Carly. Sam chuckled and raised her eyes. "Yeah, good luck with that one."

Carly shot Sam a look, then felt a finger tap on her shoulder. The figure standing behind her was truly terrifying – Spencer was dressed in a suit!

"Isn't that kind of small on you?" asked Carly, eyeing the tight sleeves and exposed ankle socks. Spencer readily agreed. "I only wore it once in tenth grade for a school play. I totally hate it!"

"You're not supposed to like it," said Carly. "It's supposed to help grandad see you as a mature adult."

"OK," nodded Spencer bravely. "But can I have ice cream after he's gone?" DING DONG!

"That's him!" gasped Carly, coming out in goosebumps. "Smells like your grandad," said Sam, sniffing the air. She leant over to Freddy and make an 'ick' face. "You smell like garbage."

"Your butt's shaped like a ham," flashed Freddie, poking his tongue out.

"Hey, no fighting tonight," pleaded Carly, chucking her friends out the back entrance. Spencer tried to straighten up, but only managed to get his arm caught in the loop of his tie.

"You figure how to get that thing tied," instructed Carly. "I'll go down and stall grandad." Spencer was a great brother. Now he just had to show Mr Shay that he was a brilliant guardian too. Sam was right, this was going to be a toughie.

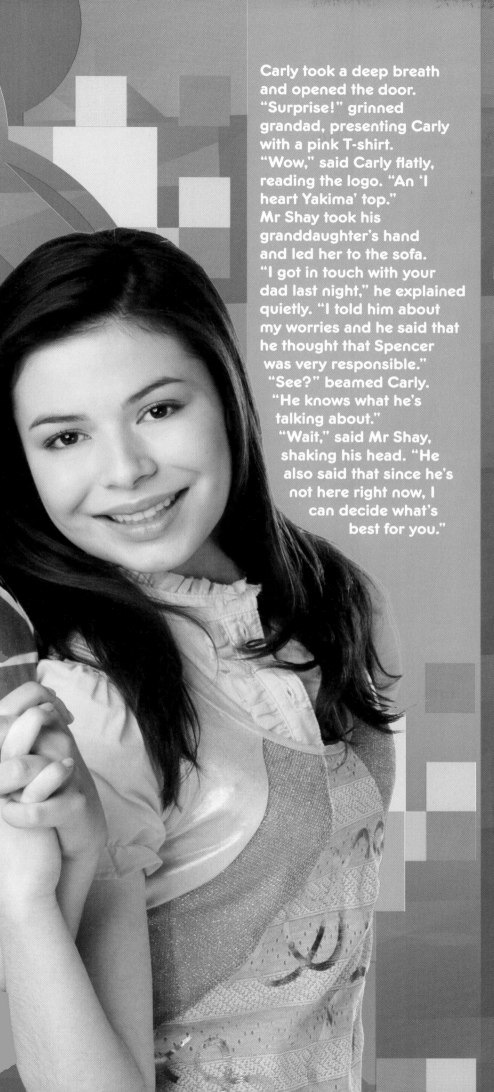

Carly took a deep breath and opened the door. "Surprise!" grinned grandad, presenting Carly with a pink T-shirt.

"Wow," said Carly flatly, reading the logo. "An 'I heart Yakima' top."

Mr Shay took his granddaughter's hand and led her to the sofa. "I got in touch with your dad last night," he explained quietly. "I told him about my worries and he said that he thought that Spencer was very responsible."

"See?" beamed Carly. "He knows what he's talking about."

"Wait," said Mr Shay, shaking his head. "He also said that since he's not here right now, I can decide what's best for you."

Carly's eyes pricked with tears. "What does he know? He's in the Navy on a submarine three miles under water! He's probably just dizzy!"

Mr Shay put his hands on his hips. It was clear that the decision had already been made.

"Please!" sobbed Carly. "I want to stay here in Seattle with Spencer."

"Spencer needs to learn to take care of himself before he can take care of a child."

Carly was getting desperate. "I'm not a child! I'm just young and short."

"Sweetheart," said Mr Shay. He couldn't bear to disappoint his granddaughter, but sometimes you had to be cruel to be kind. Realising that she wasn't going to win, Carly only had one card left to play. Right on cue, Spencer made his grand entrance.

"Hey you guys, I... OWW!!" Unused to walking in a suit, Carly's brother caught his foot on a stair. Grandad and Carly winced as he bounced off each step all the way down to the bottom. Spencer finally landed in a heap at their feet, his tie still knotted like a first-grader.

"Who's ready for dinner?" he asked, trying to recover what was clearly a very bad start to the evening.

iWanna Stay With Spencer

AFTER the arguments cut no ice, Carly and Spencer resorted to straightforward pleading. "Don't make me move to Yakima!" begged Carly, dropping to her knees. Spencer slumped down next to her. "Please don't make her move!"

Mr Shay didn't seem to know what the fuss was all about. "Yakima's a great town!" he argued.

"No great town can be named Yakima," said Carly, refusing to believe it. "It sounds like someone throwing up!" Spencer acted out a few yakking motions just to prove her point. It didn't do a great deal to prove his status as a responsible adult.

"I'm sorry," frowned Mr Shay. "She's coming to live with me." Spencer kicked the couch.

"Then I wore this monkey suit for nothing!"

While her brother battled with his irritating tie, Carly kept trying to win her grandad over. "Let me keep living here," she pleaded. "I'll be safe."

Mr Shay thought for a moment, then shook his head. He was finding it impossible to get rid of the image of the flying hammer. "Can't you see that I'm only thinking of what's best for you?" he explained, getting up to leave.

"No!" shouted Carly, following her grandad to the door. "And what about school?" Mr Shay pulled on his coat. "You can transfer to Yakima Junior High."

"Gross!"

Carly's grandad rested his hand on her shoulder. "You can have a day to pack your things and say goodbye to your friends. We leave tomorrow night."

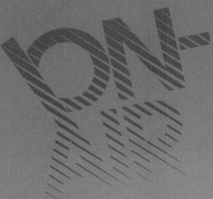

As Mr Shay pulled the door closed behind him, Carly flopped back onto the couch. Suddenly Spencer staggered back into the room, in an even worse condition than she was. His tie fixing efforts had resulted in him managing to wedge his entire arm in between his neck and the tie. "Call for help," he muttered miserably.

School the next day was utterly depressing.

"I can't believe you're leaving," groaned Sam, watching Carly empty her locker.

"Well believe it 'cos it's happening," frowned Carly. Sam and Freddie watched half-choked as Carly pulled random posters, gum and text books out of her locker. When she got to her MP3 player, Sam emotionally grasped her arm.

"Can I have this?" she asked earnestly.

Carly scowled. "I'm moving, I'm not dying."

"But don't you want me to have something to remember you by?" asked Sam. "Like 9,000 of your favourite songs!" Carly grabbed the MP3 back and shoved it in her cardboard box.

"I'm only trying to cheer you up," said Sam, nudging her in the ribs. The prospect of Carly leaving was going to rock her world from top to bottom, but if SHE broke down everybody was bound to lose it.

"You can't cheer me up," sighed Carly. "I'm going to be a Yakimite, or a Yakimaneeshian." Freddie put his hand up. "Or a Yakimaniac."

"You're Yakimannoying," grunted Sam. "So what about our show Carly?" Carly's face fell. There was no way she could do a webcast now that she was going to be 90 minutes down the motorway. Sam stamped her foot, refusing to give up.

"We need to find a way for your grandad to see that Spencer is a good guardian." Carly liked it. "I could pretend to do something really terrible."

"Riiight!" grinned Freddie. "Then Spencer will yell at you in front of grandad…"

"…which will make him realise that Spencer's a responsible authority figure," finished Sam smugly. Carly loved the idea. It was their last chance of saving her future in Seattle.

"So what bad thing are you gonna do?" asked Freddie. "I dunno," mused Carly. "Let's think of something." Sam stepped forward and put up her hand. "I enjoy this assignment."

iWanna Stay With Spencer

SPENCER stood in the kitchen peering mournfully into his wok. The time he had been dreading for the last 24 hours had almost arrived. Mr Shay popped his head round the door, causing Spencer's bottom lip to sink even lower. "I thought you weren't coming to get Carly 'til later?" he said grumpily.

His grandad shrugged. "She called me and asked me to come to dinner. Maybe she's handling this thing more maturely than you are." Spencer huffed and went back to his wok. He knew he wasn't dealing with this too well, but he just couldn't help it. "What are you cooking?" asked grandad.

"Stir-fry chicken," pouted Spencer. "Is that OK or do you want to pack up the chuck and take that to Yakima too?" Mr Shay threw his hands up. "Will you stop picking fights with me? If only you'd become a lawyer like me…"

"Hey guys," piped up a familiar voice. Grandfather and grandson span round to see Carly standing in the middle of the kitchen. Or at least it was a person that sounded like her. This kid had blue hair, body piercings and a pair of painful black leather bondage trousers. "Oh my god!" cried Mr Shay and Spencer at the same time. Carly's attempt to shock seemed to be working. "I figured that as I'm going to a new school," she breezed. "It would be the perfect time to re-invent myself. Ya like?" "Like?!" stuttered Mr Shay grimly. Spencer studied her from all angles. "You look fantastic! It's so… in your face!" Carly's heart sank – this was so not the reaction she needed! "You approve of this?" His grandad was horrified, but Spencer dragged him out of Carly's earshot. "I don't approve," he whispered. "But she's a little teenager and she's got to express herself." "What's next?" argued Mr Shay. "Swimming with hobos?" "I'm very responsible no matter what you say," hissed Spencer. "I know everything that goes on round here." Unfortunately, he'd failed to notice one important thing – a fire had broken out in his wok.

The stir fry whipped up into a blaze in seconds. While Mr Shay dialled the fire brigade, Spencer swung Carly over his shoulder and tramped her down the stairs. By the time the Shays made it to the apartment lobby, it was packed with evacuated residents. Lewbert was nearly distraught. "Too many people in here!" he shouted, flapping his arms aggressively. "I just mopped the floor!"
"Freddie texted me saying you had a fire!" said Sam, bursting through the main doors. She stood back to take in the full impact of Carly's style transformation. "Nice rods and rings."
"If you like 'em, take 'em," sighed Carly. "I already told my grandad and Spencer that they were fake."
"Why?" asked Sam.
Carly burst into tears. "'Cos Spencer thought I looked good. Then his chicken burst into flames and now I'm going to Yakima!"

Sam wanted to scream, but the sight of Freddie's mum standing behind her made her bite her lip. It was pretty clear that she'd overheard everything. "So this fire is your fault?" demanded Mrs Benson, marching over to Spencer. Spencer's shoulders dropped. "Please…"

His scary neighbour wasn't listening. "Because of you I had to stop right in the middle of rubbing anti-tick lotion on Freddie."
"Mum!" yelled Freddie. "I don't have ticks."
Mrs Benson ignored him. "They hide in your leg hair."
Freddie scowled at Sam's gleeful face. "But I don't have leg hair…"
"…which worries me deeply," argued his mum.
"I'm sorry," said Spencer. "I was making dinner and it caught fire."
Spencer gave up the fight. Who was he to argue with his grandad – he'd nearly brought down an apartment block with a single stir-fry! He walked slowly across to Mr Shay. "You were right, I am irresponsible. Carly should go live with you."
"I'm glad that you see it my way, " smiled his grandad. "You can come and visit any time you like."

iWanna Stay With Spencer

ONCE the fire crew said it was safe for everyone to go back into their apartments, it was time for Carly to fetch her cases. Freddie and Sam watched glumly as their best friend piled her stuff on the living room floor.

"OK grandad," she sighed. "I'm ready to ruin my life."

"Look I know you're upset kiddo," soothed Mr Shay. "But once you smell that Yakima air you'll feel better."

Spencer pulled a sheet off the printer and handed it to his grandad.

"It's a list of everything you need to know about Carly," he explained. "I listed all her allergies, her favourite foods and her homework schedule. I also put down the name of a good tutor 'cos she's been having some trouble with science recently."

There was a stack of info to take in.

"Thank you Spencer," answered Mr Shay. "This is impressive."

While Spencer ran through the list of Carly's vitamin tablets, Freddie braced himself to say goodbye.

"This is it," said Carly.

"Be strong Freddie!" the tech-producer gibbered, biting his fist.

After they'd dragged him away, Sam and Carly hugged each other tight.

"Will you at least try to stay out of trouble?" asked Carly.

Sam looked her best friend in the eye for a long time. "Nope."

Grandad stepped in. "We should go. Long drive, lots of traffic." Suddenly it all became too much for Freddie to bear. Stricken at the prospect of losing the love of his life, he threw himself kicking and screaming onto the floor. It was all hugely embarrassing, but what else could he do? Thankfully Sam was there to kick him in the shins. Only Spencer sat silently as Carly made her farewells.

"Aren't you gonna say goodbye to Spencer?" asked Mr Shay.

Carly stared at her big brother – still the best in the world. "We already did that before you came up," she whispered, waving to him one last time before stepping into the lift. While Sam and Freddie followed them down to the lobby, Spencer sat on his lonely couch wishing the day would end.

Just as Lewbert finished re-mopping the lobby, Carly and her friends trudged in. "OK Carly," said her grandad. "The car's right outside." "WAIT!" Everyone turned to see Spencer careering down the stairs two at a time. "You forgot this!" he cried, holding an asthma pump in his hand. "It's my inhaler," smiled Carly. "But I haven't had an asthma attack since I was seven."

Mr Shay turned to his grandson, still clutching Carly's list in his hand. "Why did you keep it all these years?" he asked. Spencer stared protectively at his little sister. "In case she needed it." Carly clearly didn't need the inhaler, but Spencer wasn't going to take any chances. "Take it," he urged. "Just in case." Mr Shay's eyes started twinkling. "Nah!" he muttered. "I'm not gonna need it." Spencer raised his eyes. "Look, asthma's tricky…" His grandfather interrupted him. "I'm not going to need this because I want Carly to stay with you." Carly's face lit up. Everybody started talking at once. Freddie fell to his knees and began kissing Mr Shay's feet.

"Can someone remove this young man from my trousers?" chuckled Carly's grandad. While Sam saved Freddie from himself, Spencer and Carly hugged. Grandad Shay agreed to drop in from time-to-time to check on how they were doing. He couldn't deny that he still thought that Spencer was a nut-bar, but he was a responsible nut-bar at least. "Is it because I lift up my shirt and rub my belly?" asked Spencer, gyrating round the lobby. "Don't do it like that," snapped Mr Shay, lifting his shirt even higher. "Do it like this." Carly giggled and showed her belly button too. Crazy tummy rubbing must have been in the family gene pool. While Lewbert screeched, Sam and Freddie joined in. Right now, they were so grateful to have Carly back they'd even consider being nice to each other.

ONCE UPON A WEBCAST

3, 2, 1 and… roll! Freddie's about to film the latest episode of iCarly, but this time the host is YOU! Draw yourself onto the screen, adding the props, outfit and green screen backgrounds you'd like to run with.

LET'S TXT!

SAM AND CARLY ARE HARDLY EVER APART. WHEN THEY HAVE TO BE SEPARATED, THEY'RE INSTANT MESSAGING EACH OTHER, AND WHEN THEY'RE NOT DOING THAT, THEY'RE TXTING ON THEIR PHONES! WANNA JAZZ UP YOUR TXTS, iCARLY STYLE? USE SAM AND CARLY'S MINI DICTIONARY TO GIVE YOU INSPIRATION, CHOOSE AN EMOTICON AND THEN LET YOUR FINGERS DO THE TALKIN'!

TXT SHORTCUTS

B4	Before
BRB	Be right back
QT	Cutie
CMON	Come on
CU	See you
FYI	For your information
THX	Thanks
TTYL	Talk to you later
UR	Your/you're
w/	With
JK	Just kidding
XLNT	Excellent
MSG	Message
L8R	Later
LOL	Laugh-out-loud
CYA	See ya
BFF	Best friends forever

EMOTICONS

#:-o	Shocked
>:-(	Annoyed
(:-*	Kiss
8-]	Wow!
:(	Sad
:-	Bored
:,(	Crying
:-)	Smile
I-0	Yawn
I-D	Big laugh
/-)	Wink
:-P	Tongue stuck out

YEP YOU GUESSED IT, that creep Nevel has been up to his sneaky tricks again! Ever since I resisted his totally GROSS attempt to chew on my cheek, the little psycho has been trying to find new ways to make me rue the day that our paths ever crossed.

Last week he had the nerve to hack into Freddie's computer, bugging the latest iCarly webcast with glitches and video mix-ups. The technical stuff was in such a mess we had to scrap the whole show 'til we got it fixed! Even though his mum had told him to write nice stuff about us on his Nevelocity. com, he just couldn't get over the fact that he'd been outsmarted by a GIRL!

There was no way that me, Sam and Freddie were going to sit back and let Nevel flush iCarly DOWN THE PAN! After a doomed attempt to break into Nev's house and hack into his PC, I put a call in to some of my dad's Navy pals.

That night, I was sooooo nervous! We had an extra cool show lined up ready for our return to the web. Somehow Spencer had managed to persuade his favourite band to play on iCarly too! Just as their first track started to kick in, Nevel's hacking caused trouble all over again. I kept my cool, smiled sweetly and waited for the reinforcements to kick in. Cue Colonel Morgan and a squadron of his top soldiers.

A WEED like Nevel was taken care of in seconds. The Navy guys confiscated his equipment and strung him up from the ceiling, while they enjoyed the rest of the show!

So if you're reading this Nevel, BACK OFF! You might think you're smart, but I'm a whole lot smarter than you are! Do it again and you'll truly RUE the day you tried to sabotage iCarly. I haven't let Sam loose on you yet, but it could be arranged...

Carly

PS. If your mum is making any more of that tapenade stuff Nevel, swing me a text.

I'M MORE THAN A MATCH FOR NEVEL

FIVE IRRITATING THINGS ABOUT NEVEL:

1. HE'S A HYGIENE FREAK »»»

Beware anyone that tries to sit on his couch without lathering their hands, arms and butt in antibacterial gel!

2. HE WEARS COLLARED SHIRTS UNDER HIS SWEATERS »»»

Per-lease! This kid is just eleven years old!

3. HE'S INTO SNIFFING HAIR »»»

His accuracy at naming a girl's shampoo from one sniff is pretty mind-blowing, but it's still a disgusting habit.

4. HE NEVER PLAYS FAIR »»»

Hacking into Freddie's computer was too devious for words!

5. HE NEEDS TO LEARN ABOUT PERSONAL SPACE »»»

He virtually sat on my lap when I went round there, YUK!

ONE GREAT THING ABOUT NEVEL:

1. HIS MUM'S TAPENADE »»»

She serves this great olive dip with cute little crispy wafers — you gotta try it!

RAVE REVIEW?

THAT SCAMP NEVEL HAS BEEN BLOGGING ON HIS WEBSITE AGAIN, BUT HAS HE GIVEN iCARLY A DECENT REVIEW THIS TIME? DETERMINED TO ONLY PASS HIS THOUGHTS ON TO THOSE IN THE KNOW, THE COWARDLY KID HAS ENCRYPTED HIS MESSAGE IN COMPUTER CODE. USE THE KEY TO DECIPHER THE SYMBOLS AND FIND OUT WHAT HE REALLY THOUGHT OF THE SHOW.

WRITE NEVEL'S BLOG IN THE SPACES BELOW.

DEAR FELLOW-WEBBERS,
I Watched the Latest
Installment of iCarly
with interest. Hot girl
Carly and spicy Sam
Really are funny, BRAVO!

::: KEY CODE :::

A = 🔡   F = ☔   K = ◖   P = 💼   U = ✋
B = 🌧   G = ≡   L = 🌙   Q = 🗄   V = ☝
C = ⛅   H = ☀   M = →   R = 📠   W = 👉
D = ☁   I = ○   N = →   S = 🄿   X = 👇
E = 🌤   J = ☾   O = →   T = 🍲   Y = 🎐   Z = 📁

WE ARE FAMILY!

WITH HER PARENTS STATIONED OVERSEAS, SPENCER'S ALL THE FAMILY THAT CARLY'S GOT LIVING UNDER THE SAME ROOF. LUCKILY THIS BROTHER AND SISTER RUB ALONG LIKE A HOUSE ON FIRE! STUDY THE TWO FAMILY PHOTOS CLOSELY. TRY AND CIRCLE SIX DIFFERENCES IN THE RIGHT-HAND PICTURE.

YUKKI YAKIMA

Carly's braved the badlands of Yakima so that she can pay grandad Shay a visit. Now it's time to come home, she and Spencer can't seem to find their way out of town. Can you pick the route that will lead them back to the Seattle before Carly gets stranded there for good?

A

B

C

YAKIMA JUNIOR HIGH

THANK YOU FOR VISITING YAKIMA! EXIT

YAKIMA TOWN MALL

Do you dream of being a webshow host like Carly and Sam? Or maybe you've got a secret talent that you're just dying to film and send over to the iCarly team! Whatever you'd like to do in front of the camera, it's important that you look your absolute best. Once your tape is out there ANYONE can see it — your mum, school friends, even your crush!

Here are the top 10 iCarly tips for looking good on screen!

1. DO A DUMMY RUN

Standing in front of the camera for the first time can be a scary prospect. Do a couple of practise cuts before you go live so that you can find your on-screen confidence.

2. AVOID BLACK, WHITE OR RED

Complete outfits in these colours just don't look right on film. If you love black, white or red, break them up with contrasting colours and tones.

3. KEEP HAIR OUT OF YOUR FACE

Flyaway locks that keep falling into your eyes will drive both you and your viewers nuts.

4. STEER CLEAR OF BUSY PATTERNS OR TEXTURES

Some crazy stripes can create a strobing effect on the screen! Avoid at all costs.

5. CHECK FOR STAINS!

Grubby clothes are a total no-no on camera.

6. IF YOU WEAR GLASSES, TIP THE FRAMES DOWN

Just lifting your specs up behind your ears a little bit should stop the lights reflecting off the lenses and creating a glare.

7. PRACTISE ON SET

Make sure that chairs and other props are set to the right height so that the camera won't cut you off in a way that makes you look too small or too tall on screen.

8. AVOID FLASHY BROOCHES, PINS OR BELT BUCKLES

These can catch the light and reflect onto the screen. Do you want your audience blinded? We think not!

9. DO A LAST-MINUTE MIRROR CALL

Just before you go on air look yourself up and down in the mirror. Any undone flies, wrongly buttoned shirts and leftover lunch on your chin could be mortifying!

10. SMILE

No one wants to watch a misery! A smile is infectious, so keep it turned on at all times.

Safe Surfing

Freddie's mum is super-careful about EVERYTHING! One area where he thinks Mrs Benson has got it sussed though, are her rules on using the internet safely. Anyone, (and we mean ANYONE) can go on the net so it's really important to take care online.

FREDDIE AND HIS FRIENDS ALL FOLLOW THESE RULES AND YOU SHOULD TOO. IF THEY'RE GOOD ENOUGH FOR MRS BENSON'S PRECIOUS BABY, THEY'RE GOOD ENOUGH FOR YOU!

Never give out your personal information online. Would you tell a stranger who you are and where you live? No way! Well chatting online is just like talking to strangers (except online, you can't even SEE them!) SO never give anyone your whole name, address or phone number on the internet, in email, in an instant message or in a chat room.

Don't use your real name in your screen name.

Keep your password to yourself. Giving out your password is like giving your brother or sister the key to your room. Do you want them in there checking out all of your stuff whenever they feel like it? NO way! Same goes for your personal stuff online.

Read the rules and privacy options for websites that let you connect with others online. We mean really read 'em. No matter which kind of site you're on, find out if you can restrict your information so that it can only be seen by the people you choose.

Only share stuff online that you don't mind anyone seeing.

42

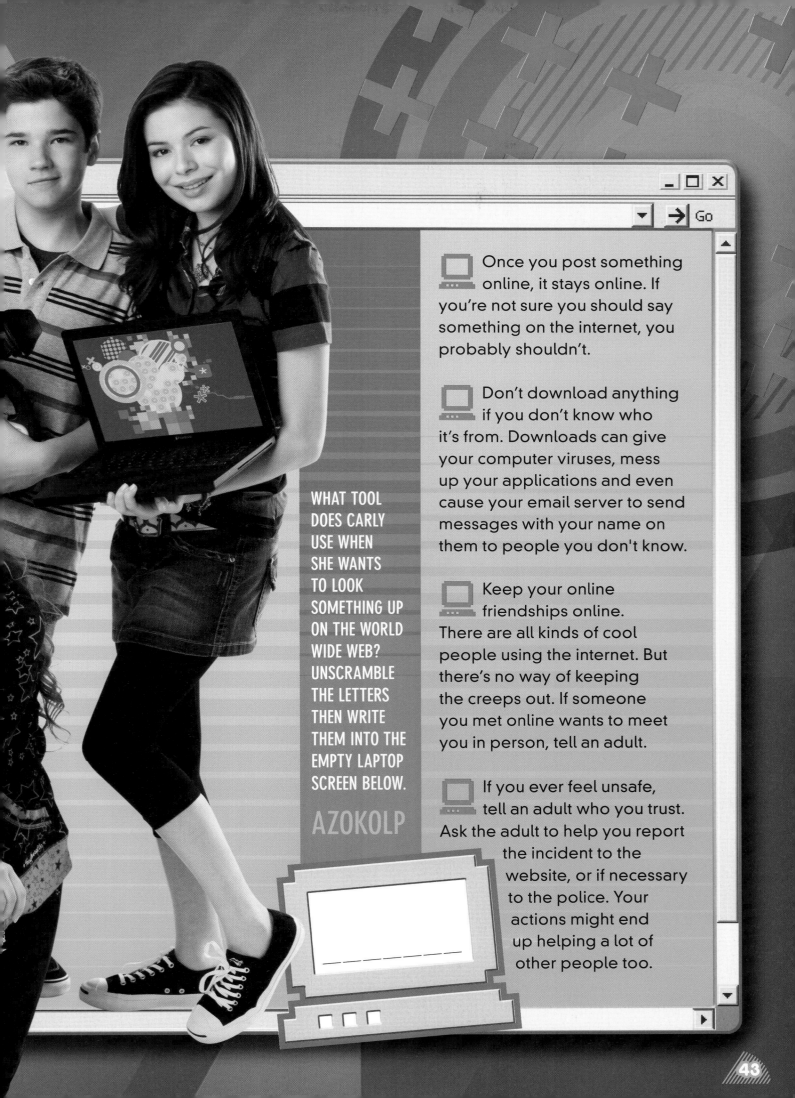

WHAT TOOL DOES CARLY USE WHEN SHE WANTS TO LOOK SOMETHING UP ON THE WORLD WIDE WEB? UNSCRAMBLE THE LETTERS THEN WRITE THEM INTO THE EMPTY LAPTOP SCREEN BELOW.

AZOKOLP

Once you post something online, it stays online. If you're not sure you should say something on the internet, you probably shouldn't.

Don't download anything if you don't know who it's from. Downloads can give your computer viruses, mess up your applications and even cause your email server to send messages with your name on them to people you don't know.

Keep your online friendships online. There are all kinds of cool people using the internet. But there's no way of keeping the creeps out. If someone you met online wants to meet you in person, tell an adult.

If you ever feel unsafe, tell an adult who you trust. Ask the adult to help you report the incident to the website, or if necessary to the police. Your actions might end up helping a lot of other people too.

iPromise NOT TO TELL

NEVER HAD A HISTORY REPORT MEANT SO MUCH TO CARLY SHAY...

SPENCER sat on the couch, his eyes fixed on the reading lamp. He had been waiting for weeks for this new gadget, now the moment of truth had arrived. "Lamp," he said slowly. "Lamp." Carly finished loading up her school backpack and trotted down the stairs. Her brother was still talking to front room furniture, but she wasn't weirded out. Compared to most of the stuff Spencer got up to, this was pretty run of the mill. "Look what I'm going to hand in today," she announced proudly. Spencer let the lamp out of his sights for a second. "You finished your history report?" "Noooo," Carly corrected him. "I finished the greatest history report in the history of history reports." "Cool," nodded Spencer, reaching out to touch it. Carly whipped the stack of papers out of his hand. She'd worked too hard on this stuff to let a grubby thumbprint spoil everything!

"Sorry, but I've got to keep this absolutely perfect. If I get an A for this, I'll get an A for this semester and I'll have straight A grades on my report card for the first time ever!" "I'm very proud of you," said Spencer, turning his attention back to the lamp. "But why won't this thing turn on? It should respond to my voice." Carly reached for the instructions. Unfortunately they were in Japanese. Suddenly Spencer's kid sister had a brainwave. "Did you try saying 'lamp' in Japanese?" Spencer was intrigued. "I did not!" Carly scanned through the pages, finally picking out the word 'rampu'. "Rampu, RAMPU," said Spencer, trying out different voices. "RAMPU!" The light flicked into action. "You just gotta say it like a really angry Japanese man!" grinned Carly. "Rampu!" As if by magic, the lamp flicked off again.

Spencer and Carly took turns shouting at the lamp, cheering every time it obeyed their angry Japanese commands. Freddie walked in to offer Carly a ride to school, then very wisely tiptoed back out again. Three hours later, Carly sat in her history lesson frantically scribbling notes off the board. Saying that Mr Devlin's class was tough was a bit like describing the bubonic plague as a mild dose of flu.

"...this was a daunting precursor to the Ignominious Defenestration of Prague," lectured Mr Devlin, dashing through a hundred years of history in no more than three breaths. Carly put her hand up. "No I will not slow down," barked the teacher, rattling off another fifteen important dates. When the bell rang a few minutes' later, every kid in the room dropped their pen out of sheer relief. "I graded your reports," said the teacher. "Pick them up on your way out." Most of the students were in for a disappointing surprise. Mr Devlin's comments ranged from 'awful' through to 'terrible', until he got to Carly. "Congratulations," he almost smiled. "Your report is the best in the class." Carly was psyched, until she looked down and saw that she'd got a... B! "Your report was excellent, but it was printed on three-hole paper," the teacher explained, "which I hate." "Just let me reprint it for you!" begged Carly, convinced that he was getting some twisted pleasure out of marking her down. Mr Devlin sniffed condescendingly "Silly little truffle. Reports can only be submitted once." Carly was distraught. "This means I'll only get a B+ for this semester!" The teacher looked face-slappingly smug. "Congratulations." "I'd like to punch three holes in him," vowed Carly the instant that Devlin had swept out of the room.

CARLY fumed all the way home from school. "Tell ya what," coaxed Sam. "On the next iCarly we'll tell everyone to go egg Mr Devlin's house." Carly shook her head. "He'd probably like it 'cos eggs don't have three holes!" Freddie followed the girls into the Shay apartment, saying wisely, "I told ya not to take his class." Before Carly could tell him where to stick his friendly advice, she was confronted by a giant obstruction in the living room.

Spencer had built a wooden letter 'A', so tall it nearly reached the ceiling! The letter was covered from base to tip in smaller 'A's painted in every colour of the rainbow. It was his latest art project and the goofy look on his face told the guys that he was hugely proud of it. "Well if it isn't my straight A little sister," whistled Spence. "Look what I'm making you!" Carly flopped on the sofa, then blurted out everything. Spencer understood at once – Devlin had been the strictest teacher in school even when he was at Ridgeway. "It was really cool of you to make this big A for me, but would you mind taking it down?" asked Carly. "I don't want to be reminded of what almost was." Spencer nodded and held out his arms. "Who needs a hug?" Carly tried her hardest not to cry, but it was tough when her big brother was being so nice to her. While Spencer comforted Carly, Sam dived on to the couch. Suddenly the new reading lamp caught her eye. "How do you turn this on?" she asked, groping for a switch. Spencer gave Carly another squeeze than fixed his eyes on the lamp. "RAMPU!"

"Why don't you use my username," said Principal Franklin, beckoning his secretary over. "Let's try it on my PC to make sure it's working."
The headteacher shot Sam a stern look of warning, before taking the foolish step of turning his back to her.
Sam started flicking the little stars and stripes flag on his desk, wondering what she was going to eat for tea that night.
"My user name is BigTeddy," he said softly, tapping on the keyboard. "And my password is pancake twenty-one."
Suddenly, Sam dropped the flag and sat up.
"This is working fine," said the Principal.
Miss Varmin smiled gratefully and bustled back to her office. Just as she got to the doorway, Principal Franklin stopped her.
"I've spilled coffee on my tie," he groaned. "What do you know about removing stains?"
Miss Varmin straightened up proudly. "I took a course in stain removal at community college!"
The Principal examined his tie one more time. The splodge of barbecue sauce wasn't too bad, but right now he was willing to do anything to postpone his latest interview with Miss Puckett.
"I'll be back in five minutes Sam," he decided.
Sam smiled sweetly. "Have fun with your stain."
As soon as the coast was clear, she nipped round to the other side of the desk. She knew it was wrong, but who was she to resist such a 24-carat opportunity?

The next day, Principal Franklin wearily glanced at his schedule. It was almost time for the low point of his week – his regular Tuesday appointment with Sam Puckett. At ten o'clock sharp, Miss Varmin showed her in.
"Good morning Sam," the Principal smiled weakly.
Sam dived in to a chair and picked up a paperweight.
"Mornin' Ted."
Mr Franklin waited for Sam to rephrase her address a little more respectfully.

"Now what trouble have you gotten yourself in this week?" he asked. Sam thought for a moment, then reeled off a list that would make most parents' eyes water. Before the Principal could consider any punishment, Miss Varmin popped her head back round the door. "I'm trying to enter the report card grades into the system, but it's not letting me log on."

iPromise
NOT TO TELL

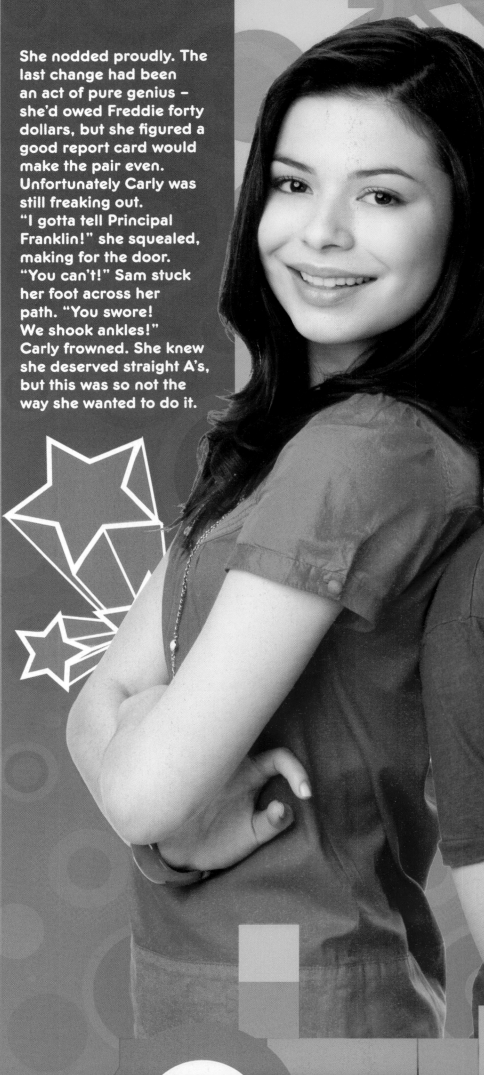

SAM couldn't wait to see her best bud at school the next day.

"What are you all whipped up about?" asked Carly. "Is it the new bacon-flavoured bubblegum?"

Sam shook her head, making a mental note to get hold of that flavour the next time she went shopping.

"You gotta swear that you won't tell anybody this," she whispered, her face breaking into a cheeky grin.

Carly nodded, but Sam wanted guarantees.

"You gotta ankle-swear."

Carly sighed, then clapped her hands together. The girls broke into an impromptu hand-slapping routine that ended with each of them shaking the other one's right ankle. It was an ancient ritual the pair reserved for their deepest and most precious secrets, the kind that were only broken on pain of death.

"Now tell me," demanded Carly.

Sam looked left and right, then spilled. "I changed your grade on the school's computer!"

Carly started to scream. Sam clamped a hand over her friend's face, realising pretty quickly that it wasn't a scream of delight.

"YOU changed my B+..." screeched Carly, totally freaking.

"...to an A+," confirmed Sam. "And I turned two of my Ds into Bs. I even bumped up one of Freddie's grades."

She nodded proudly. The last change had been an act of pure genius – she'd owed Freddie forty dollars, but she figured a good report card would make the pair even. Unfortunately Carly was still freaking out.

"I gotta tell Principal Franklin!" she squealed, making for the door.

"You can't!" Sam stuck her foot across her path. "You swore! We shook ankles!"

Carly frowned. She knew she deserved straight A's, but this was so not the way she wanted to do it.

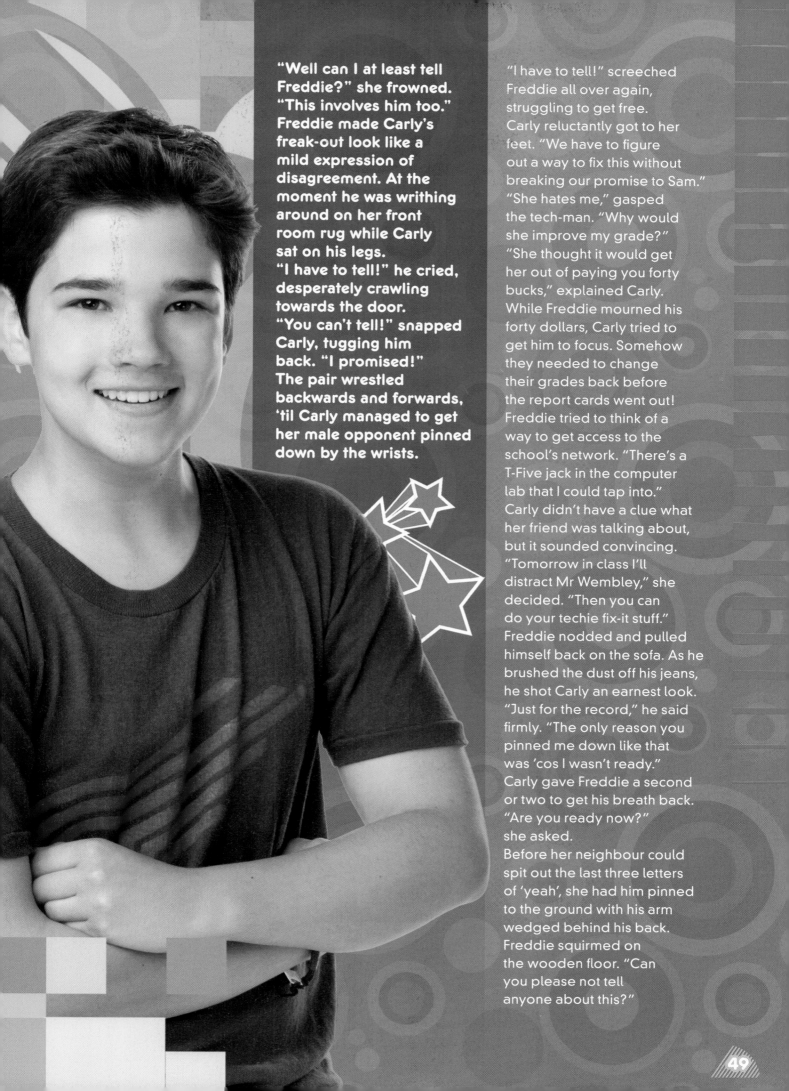

"Well can I at least tell Freddie?" she frowned. "This involves him too." Freddie made Carly's freak-out look like a mild expression of disagreement. At the moment he was writhing around on her front room rug while Carly sat on his legs.
"I have to tell!" he cried, desperately crawling towards the door.
"You can't tell!" snapped Carly, tugging him back. "I promised!"
The pair wrestled backwards and forwards, 'til Carly managed to get her male opponent pinned down by the wrists.

"I have to tell!" screeched Freddie all over again, struggling to get free. Carly reluctantly got to her feet. "We have to figure out a way to fix this without breaking our promise to Sam."
"She hates me," gasped the tech-man. "Why would she improve my grade?"
"She thought it would get her out of paying you forty bucks," explained Carly. While Freddie mourned his forty dollars, Carly tried to get him to focus. Somehow they needed to change their grades back before the report cards went out! Freddie tried to think of a way to get access to the school's network. "There's a T-Five jack in the computer lab that I could tap into." Carly didn't have a clue what her friend was talking about, but it sounded convincing. "Tomorrow in class I'll distract Mr Wembley," she decided. "Then you can do your techie fix-it stuff." Freddie nodded and pulled himself back on the sofa. As he brushed the dust off his jeans, he shot Carly an earnest look. "Just for the record," he said firmly. "The only reason you pinned me down like that was 'cos I wasn't ready." Carly gave Freddie a second or two to get his breath back. "Are you ready now?" she asked.
Before her neighbour could spit out the last three letters of 'yeah', she had him pinned to the ground with his arm wedged behind his back. Freddie squirmed on the wooden floor. "Can you please not tell anyone about this?"

iPromise NOT TO TELL

AS she took her seat in Mr Wembley's computer studies class, Carly felt her heart thumping like a drum. Freddie pulled out a chair next to her. He was trying to act casual, but his face had already flushed to the colour of a ripe beetroot. Mr Wembley asked the class to log on, before presenting them with an exceptionally dull exercise to complete. "I'll keep him distracted," whispered Carly. "You go tap into the B-Five line." Freddie shook his head. "It's called a T-Five." "Like it matters!" screeched Carly sarcastically. "Just go!" Freddie thought he'd try the 'blunt pencil' routine. He grabbed a pencil and sauntered over to the sharpener on the wall next to Mr Wembley's desk. Carly's hand shot up. "I have a question please!"

While the teacher's back was turned, Freddie sank to his knees behind Mr Wembley's desk. There was the jack, just behind the waste paper basket! Freddie carefully pulled a screwdriver out of his trouser pocket. All he had to do was remove the plate covering the T-Five and make a few modifications... Freddie worked as fast as he could, but Carly was running out of questions. "Why are there two shift keys?" she babbled, as Mr Wembley began to make his way back to his desk.

The teacher's face creased with irritation. He'd much rather have been on his own tinkering with his PC than be surrounded by pesky kids asking dumb questions. "Just do your work please," he begged, turning his back on Carly. Desperate times called for desperate measures. With a loud squeal, Carly closed her eyes and fainted onto the floor in front of her classmates. Across the other side of the room Freddie gulped. He was almost done, but there were still two screws to put back in place! Mr Wembley leapt over and pulled Carly back onto her chair. "Are you all right?" he asked, fanning her face. Carly came round, then spotted that Freddie still had work to do. "Ooohh!" she cried, swooning all over again.

As soon as the bell rang for end of class, Carly and Freddie sprinted home like a couple of roadrunners. The friends tore into Carly's loft, booted up Freddie's computer then put his tech skills to the test.
"OK," said Freddie, focussing. "Generating random codes." The laptop answered with a loud `PING`.

"Sweet!" concluded Freddie. "We're past the school's firewall, which gives us access to everything." The friends couldn't believe the amount of info swimming around on the school's network. Grades, staff salaries and canteen menus – it was all here.

"Hey, it's Principal Franklin's birthday today!" smiled Carly. Freddie nodded, but kept on scrolling. "Wait!" shrieked Carly, spotting this week's lunch menu. "Would it hurt anybody if we changed spinach to hash browns?" Even Freddie couldn't deny the clear benefits of such a change – who apart from Miss Briggs would be disappointed at being deprived of their spinach? A quick type on the keyboard and it was done. "Here are the student grades," he added, spotting Carly's name in another box on the screen.

`KNOCK! KNOCK! KNOCK!`
Carly and Freddie exchanged nervous looks. Spencer was in the bath, Sam was at the diner and Freddie's mum always barged right in – so who was at the door?
The visitors didn't wait to be invited. Two brawly agents in dark uniforms broke the lock and burst into the living room.
"Computer Security Agency!" cried one, holding a very grown-up looking badge. "Step away from that laptop." The kids put their hands above their heads.
"You two go to Ridgeway Junior High?" asked the other, picking up his radio. Carly nodded despairingly.
"We were advised of a breach in the school's computer network this afternoon, then tracked it to your wireless uplink," said the first officer. Even if that wasn't clear, one thing was. Carly Shay and Freddie Benson were in a whole lotta trouble.

iPromise NOT TO TELL

 **CARLY** and Freddie perched anxiously on the sofa, while Principal Franklin spoke with the CSA agents. As Carly's legal guardian, Spencer opted to fix the drinks. Having the headmaster in their house was totally weird, but then it had been one of those weeks.

"This just doesn't make any sense," said Mr Franklin. "These two have always been such well-behaved students." Freddie leant forward, then whispered in Carly's ear. "We have to tell them." Carly had to agree that it was a tempting option. However a promise-was-a-promise-was-a-promise.

The Principal called the duo over. "These agents insist that you were hacking into the school's computer, but I know that neither of you would…"

"We did hack into the network," interrupted Carly, singing like a canary. "But it was only to find out when your birthday was."

"Right," said Freddie, cottoning on. "We wanted to give you a present." The Principal dismissed the agents with a wave of his hand. Carly's story sounded plausible and besides, he liked presents. "So what d'ya get me?" he beamed.

"Wait here!" ordered Carly in a panic.

The pair tore into the kitchen and returned with… a microwave. While the Principal checked out the wattage, Carly made a mental note to kill Sam when she saw her next.

The following day, the report cards were mailed out as planned.

"I feel dirty," scowled Freddie, ashamed of his good grades.

As soon as Sam breezed past, Carly grabbed her by the backpack. "I had to lie and give away my microwave because of you!" she shrieked, telling the whole sad story of their clash with the CSA.

"Did you guys rat me out?" Sam asked accusingly.

"We had to lie to keep your dirty secret safe!" shouted Freddie.

"It gets easier I promise," said Sam, cheering up. "Soon you'll be able to lie and feel nothing at all."

"Hey!" cheered Spencer, when Carly and Sam got in from school. "You're a liar!" Carly flinched then noticed with a groan that he'd resurrected the giant A sculpture. The mail must have come. Spencer duly held up his sister's perfect report card. "You said that you weren't gonna get straight A's, but you did and I am so proud of you!" Sam cut in. "You should be. She earned that grade." Spencer beamed, then stepped back so they could take in the full majesty of his A sculpture. "This can be a permanent reminder of what you did." "'Ain't that the truth," muttered Carly under her breath. Spencer reached behind the sofa, as he explained that he'd called their dad to share the good news.

Carly gasped as he pushed out an expensive flat screen TV with a pink bow stuck on the front. "Dad asked me to buy this big TV for your room!" beamed Spencer, wondering why his little sister didn't look even faintly excited. Carly made a bolt for her bedroom, tortured by her crime. "I have so many nice things. Can we give it to a hobo or something?" she screeched down the stairs.

Just when she thought things couldn't get any worse, they duly did. Unable to sleep a wink all night, Carly braved school in a pair of dark sunglasses. Forty-two inches of high definition guilt standing in the corner of her bedroom had been too much to bear. Sam greeted Carly and Freddie in the hall, then dragged them over to the student's noticeboard. "You made the top ten of the honour's list Carly," she smiled. "Your grades pushed Karen Yamakawa right off the chart." Just then Karen Yamakawa walked past, sobbing. Carly could barely live with herself – Karen was one of the hardest-working students she knew!

iPromise NOT TO TELL

THAT week's webcast was a half-hearted affair. Carly tried to be her usual upbeat, crazy self, but it just wasn't happening. While Sam introed some random videos, Carly's mind buzzed with the guilt of her ill-gotten grades. "I can't take this anymore!" she suddenly blurted out when Freddie turned the camera back on her.

Carly burst out of the studio and clattered down the stairs. Spencer was up a ladder in the living room, putting the last proud 'A' on his giant sculpture. "I didn't get straight A's!" she yelled, interrupting his creative flow.

Spencer put down his letter in surprise – wasn't she meant to be presenting iCarly? "Mr Devlin gave me a B+ then Sam changed my grade on the school computer!" bellowed Carly, totally out of control. "Freddie and I tried to change it back but then we got caught. I lied to Principal Franklin, made Karen Yamakawa cry and now my hair's falling out with the guilt!"

Spencer carefully considered the implications of his little sister's revelation. "So I have to take apart my big 'A' again?"

Carly dived on the sofa and buried her head in a cushion. "I promised Sam that I wouldn't tell anybody."

"Did you ankle-shake on it?" asked Spencer.

A howl of despair from the sofa confirmed the seriousness of the situation. Spencer climbed down the ladder, just as Freddie and Sam made it into the living room. "The guilt is eating me alive!" cried Carly. "Tell me what to do." Spencer glanced over to Sam, paused for a maddeningly long amount of time, then replied in a loud voice. "Sometimes doing what's right is more important than keeping a promise."

Carly kept her head out of the cushion while she thought things over. When Spencer also pointed out that she'd managed to get one of the 'A's from his sculpture fixed to her butt, she wondered if she'd ever show her face again.

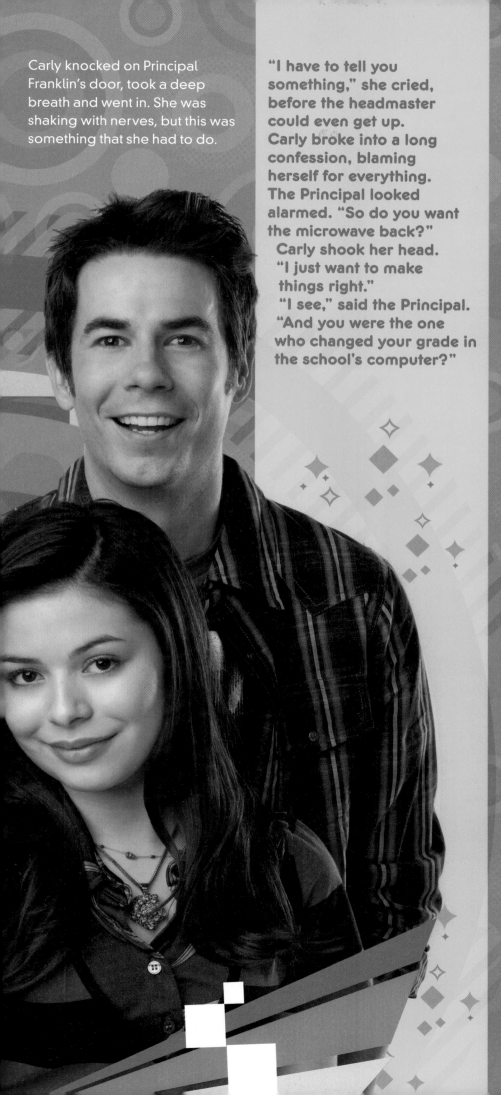

Carly knocked on Principal Franklin's door, took a deep breath and went in. She was shaking with nerves, but this was something that she had to do.

"I have to tell you something," she cried, before the headmaster could even get up. Carly broke into a long confession, blaming herself for everything. The Principal looked alarmed. "So do you want the microwave back?"

Carly shook her head. "I just want to make things right."

"I see," said the Principal. "And you were the one who changed your grade in the school's computer?"

"Yes sir," Carly replied sadly. The Principal rubbed his chin and started staring into the corner of the room. Completely thrown, Carly turned round to see Freddie sat in a chair behind her! "Hiya!" he waved sheepishly, before admitting that he had just confessed the same thing! Suddenly Sam walked in, with a fierce look on her face. "It was me alright?" she announced. "I hacked the computer and I changed the grades."

"Now that I believe," said Principal Franklin, pleased to have untangled the mess. Sam had more to say. "The only reason they didn't tell on me was 'cos I made them promise. I was wrong to do that to a friend." Carly and Sam hugged.

"I think under the circumstances that you and Freddie are off the hook," grinned the Principal, setting Sam detention twice a week for six weeks. Sam wasn't phased, it was just a relief to make everything alright again. Just then the bell rang.

"Time for assembly," said Principal Franklin. "Shall we?" The gang followed the headmaster out of the room, but old habits die hard. Once he was out of sight, Sam did a U-turn and got herself comfortable at Franklin's computer.

"Let's make my detention once a week for two weeks," she smiled, merrily tapping the keys. Just before she could press the enter button, Carly scooted back in. This time Sam found herself being dragged to assembly by the hair.

QUICK EPISODE QUIZ

QUESTION 1

Why did Carly's grandad visit her in 'iWanna Stay With Spencer'?

A) To wish her happy birthday.

B) To take her back to Yakima.

C) To check out Spencer's latest artwork.

QUESTION 2

What is the name of Jake's ex-girlfriend in 'iLike Jake'?

A) Veronica.

B) Janine.

C) Stephanie.

QUESTION 3

What artwork does Spencer create for his hero in 'iHeart Art'?

A) A mini version of the Eiffel Tower.

B) An oil painting

C) A yo-yo sculpture.

Reckon you know every episode of iCarly off by heart?
Test your expert credentials by taking this multiple choice quiz!

QUESTION 4
What sort of dancing does Miss Briggs' do in Sam's 'iDream of Dance' nightmare?

A) Scottish Highland dancing.

B) Salsa.

C) Ballet.

QUESTION 5
What does Spencer vow to do after his ordeal in 'iScream on Hallowe'en'?

A) Never forget to buy candy for trick or treaters.

B) Always wear his Dracula fangs.

C) Go to bed with the lights on.

QUESTION 6
How many chicks go missing in 'iHatch Chicks'?

A) Six.

B) Two.

C) A dozen.

QUESTION 7
Why does Carly's show get disrupted in 'iRue the Day'?

A) Mrs Benson stomps into the studio.

B) Nevel hacks into Freddie's tech equipment.

C) There's a power cut half way through.

QUESTION 8
What dish does Spencer serve for Freddie and Valerie in 'iWant to Date Freddie'?

A) Spaghetti Tacos.

B) Spaghetti Bolognaise.

C) Spaghetti Carbonara

QUESTION 9
Who is the iCarly team's creepy stalker in 'iAm Your Biggest Fan'?

A) Spencer's mate Socko.

B) A girl called Mandy.

C) Lewbert.

lol

QUESTION 10
What happens to Carly and Sam's poster in 'iWant More Viewers'?

A) It gets lost.

B) It blows away.

C) It gets smudged in the rain.

UNDER 3: Get back online – you gotta whole lot of homework to do before you become a gold star iCarly fan!

3–7: Not bad, you certainly like checking in with the Ridgeway crew! Catch a few more episodes and you could be on the team.

8–10: Top of the class! Even Sam Puckett has to admit she's impressed!

SPENCER'S RADICAL RECIPE

You are so LUCKY! Spencer is gonna show you how to make a dessert from his favourite bakery, Galini's! They sell an amazing coconut cream pie, but when poor old Mr Galini died Spence had to date his granddaughter Trudy in order to get hold of the secret recipe. Trudy's not exactly babelicious, but it was well worth it – wait 'til you taste that pie...

MR. GALINI'S   _ □ ✕

COCONUT CREAM PIE!

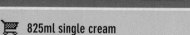

INGREDIENTS   _ □ ✕

- 🛒 825ml single cream
- 🛒 2 eggs
- 🛒 175g granulated sugar
- 🛒 60g plain flour
- 🛒 ¼ teaspoon salt
- 🛒 275g desiccated coconut
- 🛒 ¾ teaspoon vanilla extract
- 🛒 1 240g ready made sweet pastry case
- 🛒 284ml double cream

1. In a medium saucepan, combine the single cream, eggs, sugar, flour and salt.

2. Bring the mixture to a gentle boil over a low heat, stirring continuously.

3. Take the pan off the heat and stir in ¾ of the dessicated coconut then drop in all of the vanilla extract.

4. Pour the coconut mix into the pastry case and chill 2 to 4 hours, or until firm.

5. In a separate bowl, pour in the double cream and then mix it with a whisk on a medium speed. Keep going until the cream is solid enough to form soft peaks. Now stir in the rest of the coconut.

6. Spread the whipped coconut cream over the top of the chilled pie and then serve to your nicest friends. Yumtastic!

+++ HEY KIDS! DON'T TRY TO WHIP UP A COCONUT CREAM PIE WITHOUT THE HELP OF A (RESPONSIBLE) ADULT LIKE ME – GOT IT? +++

ACROSS

1. Sam's surname (7).

2. Miss Briggs' Christian name (8).

3. Carly, Sam and Freddie's Junior High School (9).

4. The iCarly team's hometown (7).

5. Spencer's profession (6).

6. The name of Carly's Principal (8).

DOWN

1. Nasty Nevel's surname (9).

2. A corn shell that Spencer likes to fill with spaghetti (4).

3. Bushwell Plaza's not-so- friendly doorman (7).

4. Carly's history teacher (6).

Think you're smart? Have a go at Carly's fantabulous new crossword. Try and fill in every square using the clues next to the grid.

iCarly CROSSWORD

HOW TO MAKE YOUR OWN WEBSHOW

START WITH A HOT IDEA ▼

Before you can film a thing, you need to sit down with a notepad and devise the idea that will be the basis of your show. Is it going to feature comedy impressions, interviews with local celebrities or singing and dancing routines? Once your idea's in place you can think up a catchy programme name.

WRITE THE SCRIPT ▼

Your first episode has to be a knockout. Although you might be confident at improvising on screen, you should at least draw up a schedule with rough running times allocated to each item.

DRESS THE SET ⊕ ▼

Where are you going to choose as the studio for your new show? Your back garden, a conservatory or a well-lit garage could all work well. Once you've checked with an adult, think about any decorations that you'd like to add to the backdrop.

RECRUIT A CREW ▼

Filming iCarly would never happen if Freddie and Sam weren't involved too! Find some family members or friends that would like to take part in the show,

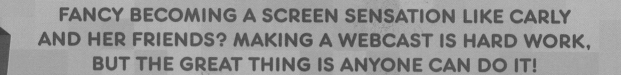

CARLY'S QUICK TIPS

PLAN IT OUT!

Sam and I don't just turn up in front of the camera each week and talk RUBBISH! Ok so we do talk rubbish sometimes, but each episode follows a planner so we know exactly what's coming up next.

BORING'S BORING, RUDE'S JUST RUDE!

You don't have to be rude to be funny and you don't have to talk for hours. Keep your webcast short and snappy and your audience will keep coming back for MORE! Cut out any swearing, it 'ain't big or clever.

EXPERIMENT!

Keep the show fresh by trying new things every week. Daft props, comedy sound effects and surprise guests will make sure that your viewers stay on their toes.

then decide who should do what. The roles of director, camera person and co-host are all up for grabs!

FILM FANTASTIC

When you start recording your first episode, be prepared to make a few mistakes. It's also good to experiment with different camera angles, so that the picture looks as clear as possible. Check out the light and adjust your positions so that shadows don't fall across the hosts' faces.

GET EDITING

Once the show's in the bag, you're ready to upload your movie clips onto your PC and edit them together. Now's the time to cut out the bloopers or segments that simply run on too long. Techno whizzes like Freddie might also want to slot in some special effects.

GET IT OUT THERE

Once your webcast is ready, you need to find an audience. Do you just want to invite a few friends over to watch it, or do you have bigger plans? Check with an adult and then upload your footage onto a movie sharing website and see what responses you get. If people like it, they'll soon tell you! Don't take your reviews too seriously, but if you get any interesting comments remember them for next time.

ALWAYS CHECK WITH AN ADULT BEFORE USING A VIDEO CAMERA AND UPLOADING ANYTHING ONTO THE NET.

SAM'S BRILLIANT BLOG!

THE SPOOKIEST NIGHTMARE EVER!

MISS BRIGGS IS SO NOT MY FAVOURITE PERSON – I just don't know why she's got it in for me. She's always putting me on the detention for the slightest things! Sleeping in class, beating up Freddie and eating breakfast at my desk are all complete no-nos whenever she's around. B.O.R.I.N.G! The other day, she managed to drag her lesson down to a new low. As a 'special treat' (tsk), she invited loony dancer Benjamin Yip to perform for the class! Everybody boo-ed like crazy, but of course yours truly gets lumbered with a DETENTION again. I naturally blamed the boos on Gibby, but Briggs wasn't having a bit of it.

Benjamin Yip's Scottish Highland dancing was just as lame as we thought it was gonna be – Miss Briggs should have listened to us! By the end of the hour, we were literally BEGGING to be released so that we could go on to double science! After that me and Carly decided to ask iCarly viewers to submit videos of their coolest dance moves. Sounds like a good idea? WRONG! Over 3,000 kids sent in their clips. Some were cool, some were lame and a frighteningly high percentage were totally demented! Carly, Freddie and I were up night after night watching kids from all over the country busting moves on video. By the time we got to the last 20 I was seriously LOSING THE WILL TO LIVE!! That must have been when I passed out on Carly's couch. While I was catchin' flies I had this insane dream that I was back in Miss Briggs' classroom. YIKES! Suddenly she whipped out an electric bagpipe and started playing this crazed Highland JIG. The worst thing about it? I couldn't stop dancing either! There I was locked in a horrendous dance-off, skipping like a demented chicken to the drone of bagpipes! Even now, the memory brings me out in COLD SWEATS!!

Sam

Webnut23 asks:
What did you do when you woke up?

Sam: After slapping myself several times with the remote control, I headed to the kitchen for a late night pick-me-up. A triple layer PB&J sandwich was just what I needed to DETOX the freaky memory of Miss Briggs prancing about in a kilt.

SuperSmoothie asks:
Who's the best dancer out of you, Carly and Freddie?

Sam: Carly's not bad, but I would have to say ME. Have you SEEN Freddie dance? Imagine a short-sighted spaniel with two left feet. Totally PATHETIC!

Freddie: Hey, Freddie here. That is so not true Puckett! I can bust a move when I want to, I just choose not to show my artistic side whenever you're within a five-mile radius.

SOUNDS LIKE...

The iCarly team never stop talkin'! Use your knowledge of the gang to match up the right character with the right quote.

1 CARLY

2 SAM

 **A.** EVERYONE CHILLAX.

 **B.** YOU KNOW MY DIGITS!

 **C.** MY BABY SISTER IS A WEBSTAR!

 **D.** STOP DOING BAD THINGS!

3 FREDDIE

4 SPENCER

ART ATTACK!

Spencer's style of art is pretty weird sometimes! His crazy recycled sculptures can be thought-provoking, exciting and even downright dangerous. How wacky is your mind? Fill this frame with your sketch for a brand new masterpiece.

WHAT'S YOUR TALENT?

1. TRICKY _ _ _ _ _ _ _ _ _

ANAGRAM CLUE: ACINGIAM

★ Perform a close-up card trick.
★ Pull something crazy out of a hat.
★ Saw your best friend in half (only kidding!)

2. _ _ _ _ _ _ _ STAR

ANAGRAM CLUE: TORPSS

★ See how many press-ups you can do in 30 seconds.
★ Wow them with a gymnastics feat.
★ Spin a football on your finger.

3. ONSCREEN _ _ _ _ _ _ _

ANAGRAM CLUE: TIRTAS

★ Build a sculpture live on air.
★ Do a funny caricature of a celebrity.
★ Splatter paint on a giant strip of lining paper.

What video would you like to mail to iCarly? Don't panic if you can't sing or dance, everybody's good at something! Last week, Sam wowed the crowds with a burped version of the national anthem, so beat that!!

Six types of web act are listed below, along with some suggested clip ideas. Fill in the name for each one by unscrambling the anagram clues.

When you've worked out all six talents, decide which one you'd be best at. Colour in the star next to your choice.

4. COOL _ _ _ _

ANAGRAM CLUE: OKOC

★ Whip up the ultimate TV dinner.
★ Build a super-wacky sandwich.
★ Make the world's most awesome ice cream sundae.

5. CRAZY _ _ _ _ _ _ _ _

ANAGRAM CLUE: DONACEMI

★ Make up and present your own joke.
★ Impersonate a member of your family.
★ Relive a hilarious true story.

6. _ _ _ _ _ _ _ _ QUEEN

ANAGRAM CLUE: NANGCID

★ Perform a routine to your favourite track.
★ Invent a crazy new style of movement.
★ Choreograph a large group number featuring all your friends.

iHatch CHICKS

Sam was a great best friend, except when it came to science projects...

CARLY patiently loaded her locker, waiting for Sam to finish her rant. "I can't believe that Mr Soo-Mack gave us another project," she blasted. "Who does he think he is?"

"Our science teacher?" guessed Carly.

Sam raised her eyes, still insulted at the prospect of homework. "At least he paired us up together." Carly suddenly started burrowing into her stuff, trying not to catch her best friend's eye.

"You're bummed out that we've been put together!" gasped Sam, not able to believe it! Carly slammed the locker door and sighed. "It's just that every time we get paired up I end up doing all the work."

Sam wasn't going to protest with that one, but before she could say another word Freddie turned up looking equally depressed. As always, he'd been desperate to work with Carly on the science project. Not only had he lucked out to Sam, Mr Soo-Mack had paired him up with psycho wrestler Duke.

"Whassup Fred-doe!" Duke lumbered over, yanking Freddie into a half-nelson. Carly distracted the meathead with a beef jerky from her lunchbox, while Sam dragged Freddie free. How was a mild-mannered tech-producer going to survive this whole science project?

Back home that night, Carly and Sam sat down to pick a theme for their project. Carly tossed out three or four options, while Sam suggested blowing stuff up in the microwave.

"You know when I was at school we hatched a bunch of baby chicks in the classroom," said Spencer. "Very cool, very fun."

Carly clapped her hands. "Yes! Can we do it here?"

Spencer nodded. "You could even show the whole process on iCarly!"

Sam approved. "And then we can make fried chicken."

"Five, four, three, two…" iCarly was just about to go on air. Carly and Sam leapt into shot, dressed in board shorts and bikinis.

"She's the fantabulous Carly…" grinned Sam.

"…and she's Sam, my poorly behaved best friend!" quipped Carly. "Look at us on the beach!"

The girls started surfing while Freddie played a cool Hawaiian beach scene on the green screen behind them. It looked awesome!

"Ahhhhhh!!"

Suddenly the beach footage flicked and changed to show a spinning planet hurtling through outer space.

"Surely it's dangerous to be in outer space in just our swimsuits!" cried Carly.

"Turn off the special effects!" Freddie flicked to a new segment, giving Sam the cue to pull a sheet off the table beside her. Underneath was a cool incubator with six eggs inside.

"We got some fertilised chicken eggs for our science project," explained Carly. "This glass box keeps them at 99.5 degrees."

Sam gently pressed her face to the incubator. "All we gotta do is turn the eggs a few times every day and soon we're gonna have us some baby chicks!"

"Come back to iCarly anytime you want and click on the Egg Cam button," beamed Carly. "You can watch our little egglings every day until they are born!"

The friends introduced the tiny webstars one by one. Shelly was joined by Huevo, Omlette, Benedict, Yoko and Poachy.

"Okay family photo," ordered Carly, crouching down beside her co-parent.

iHatch CHICKS

AT the weekend, Sam had invited herself for a sleepover. Now the girls were sprawled across the couch in their PJs watching trash TV.

"I want breakfast," muttered Sam.

"We got cereal," replied Carly, even though she couldn't be bothered to move.

Sam pulled back the blanket she'd been hiding under. "Milk?"

Carly winced. "Outta milk."

Sam wasn't phased. "I'll use root beer."

Before the girls could raid the kitchen, Spencer came out of the shower. He was still wrapped in a towel and dripping on the rug.

"Uh you guys?" he asked, holding out his cupped hands. "Any reason I just found this in my shower?"

Spencer carefully opened his hands. There, sat on his palm was the cutest, fluffiest little chick the girls had ever seen. It chirruped a cute hello, blinking in the light.

Sam and Carly looked at each other, then freaked.

"I picked her up thinking she was a bar of soap," explained Spencer, visibly shaken. "Good thing I realised before... never mind."

"But how could there be a chick in there?" asked Sam.

Carly nodded. "Our chicks haven't hatched yet."

The girls paused for a moment, then caught each other's eye.

"We're MOTHERS!!" screamed Carly, taking the stairs up to the studio two at a time.

Carly and Sam raced over to the incubator. It was empty apart from a whole bunch of cracked eggshells! Freddie tore in behind them. "I was watching the Egg Cam!" he gasped, out of breath. "I can't believe they've already hatched!"

Carly took a closer look at the incubator. A little chicky escape route had been made where the lid wasn't fixed on properly.

"Aww man," scowled Freddie. "Did Sam eat them?"

Sam was outraged. "I wouldn't eat baby chicks! Not raw anyway!"

"If Spencer found one in the bathroom downstairs, the other chicks could be anywhere in this whole apartment," warned Sam.

Freddie scratched his head. "Don't newborn chicks have to stay in their incubator?"

"They do!" squealed Carly. "We gotta find out how long they can be out for."

The gang ran over to Freddie's technical trolley. Freddie pulled Zaplook onto his laptop and searched for 'chicks'. In seconds, a full Chickapaedia flashed onto the screen.

Carly read out loud. "During the first week of life, newborn chicks must be kept at temperatures of 90 degrees, and they must be fed every four hours."

"Or else what?" asked Sam.

"Bad things," was all Carly could manage as an answer. Freddie scrolled back through the Egg Cam. "According to this, they got out 56 minutes ago."

"If Spencer found one," answered Sam. "We've still got five chicks missing. That gives us three hours and four minutes to find 'em."

Carly went white. "We gotta do it! Otherwise we've got five cute little chicken funerals on our hands!"

Freddie looked determined. Even though he had his own science nightmare to sort out, there was no way he was gonna let those chicks face the perils of the outside world. "Duke's on his way over to work on our project," he cried. "He can help too."

"We're in the middle of a crisis!" barked Carly. "This is not a time for sweaty wrestlers!"

"The more on it the better," answered Freddie. "Let's go!"

Sam had one last question before the hunt began. "Can we have breakfast first?"

"Noo!" yelled Carly and Freddie at the same time.

"OK, OK," answered Sam defensively. Some people were just so touchy in the mornings!

iHatch CHICKS

SPENCER slung on some clothes, then everyone gathered in the living room for a team briefing. Freddie set the incubator up by the couch, then added a bowl of birdseed for the chick.

"OK, so there's six chicks," said Carly, pointing to the whiteboard behind her. "Spencer already found Shelly in the shower." Spencer picked up a red pen and placed a big tick next to the sketch of Shelly. "Checkin' off Shelly."

"That means that we've got five chicks on the loose in the apartment," added Carly. Sam raised her hand. "How much longer can they go without eating?"

Carly checked her mobile. "Two hours, fifty-five minutes." "Didn't the Chickapaedia say that newborn chicks had to be kept at 90 degrees?" Spencer hurtled over to the thermostat. The apartment was only 72!

"Turn it up!" ordered Carly, cranking up the operation. Next she handed out walkie talkies to everyone. Freddie was allocated the third floor, Spencer had to check the bedrooms and Sam was told to turn over the living room. Carly eyed everyone seriously as she made her way towards the kitchen. "Grab a walkie talkie and find a small chicken," she said firmly. "Now!"

The guys swarmed in all directions, each on a high state of chicken alert. Sam started frantically chucking cushions off the sofa, while Carly shook the biscuit tins stacked across the kitchen worktop. It was a highly pressurised situation. Everybody was tense, uptight and sweating out, but those chickens had to be saved.

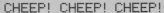

CHEEP! CHEEP! CHEEP!

Carly glanced at the kitchen sink, then did a double take. In the heat of the moment, she abandoned the walkie talkie and bellowed into the front room.

"Hey!" she shouted. "I think I found one!"

Spencer and Sam both screeched into the kitchen at the same time.

"There's a peep coming from the sink," explained Carly. "Maybe he fell down the drain!"

The trio crouched down to listen. There was definitely a cheeping noise coming out of the tap! Carly tried to stare down the plughole, but it was too dark.

"I'll turn on the light," decided Spencer, flicking a switching underneath the unit.

"Nooooo!" screeched Carly, but it was too late. Everybody grimaced as the waste disposal rattled into action!

"Oh my god!" gasped Spencer, flicking everything back off again as quick as he could.

Carly thought she was going to lose it, but when they listened again the cute little cheep cheep sound was still there.

"Okay," puffed Spencer. "That was close."

Carly clutched her heart. "You almost made a baby chicken smoothie."

Their little experiment had shown that the chickie was definitely stuck in the pipe underneath the sink. Carly cleared stuff out from underneath then grabbed a wrench from Spencer.

"You go find the other four," she directed. "Sam and I got this one!"

Five minutes' later, Carly had the pipe unscrewed, but her hand was too big to fit in and pull out the chicken! Sam bent down to assess the situation.

"Right, cup your hands," she ordered.

Carly shrugged. "Why?"

"Just do it!" snapped Sam. "Here's where two miserable years of trombone lessons pay off."

Sam wiped her mouth with the back of hand, then blew into the drain pipe with all of her might. Moments later, a little yellow chick fluttered out of the cylinder at breakneck speed.

"Gotcha!" beamed Carly, catching the youngster in both hands. "Only four to go!"

iHatch CHICKS

Freddie frantically searched the upstairs studio, Carly popped little Huevo back into the incubator. Spencer cheered then ran over to place another tick on his chart. "Huevo's bueno. Four to go." Just then, Duke arrived. Carly was underwhelmed to see him, but had to admit that they could still do with some help in the search. "Shhhh!" said Spencer, calling the kids over to the window. A very faint cheeping sound was coming from the heating duct! "Help me move this thing," cried Spencer, dragging his workbench out of the way. Carly got down on her hands and knees. "I'll crawl in and get him." Spencer dramatically moved his kid sister to one side. "Too dangerous I'm afraid. I got this one." It was a tight fit, but Spencer managed to stick his head into the vent and then wriggle his body half way in. The chick was right there in front of him, only a few centimetres beyond his nose. Only problem was that his arms were now pinned to his side. "Hey guys!" yelled Spencer, trying hard not to sound desperate. "Uncle Spencer is stuck!" To make things worse, the chick began to hop even deeper into the ventilation shaft. Spencer tried sucking the air to vacuum the little bird back towards him, but it was hopeless.

Freddie ran down the stairs, just as Spencer's frustration was turning to full-on panic. "Will you guys pull me outta here?" he cried hopefully. Carly, Sam, Freddie and Duke all grabbed onto Spencer's ankles. The kids yanked so hard, his jeans came right off. Unfortunately they weren't followed by Carly's big brother. "Please tell me I'm wearing underwear!" howled Spencer.

Carly bent her head down and back up again very quickly. No one was more relieved than her when the answer came back positive. "Relax!" said Freddie, using his not un-sizable science brain. "The heat's on high which will eventually cause the metal to expand." "And you'll get all sweaty," added Sam helpfully. Spencer heroically braced himself for the long wait. "You go and find the other chicks."

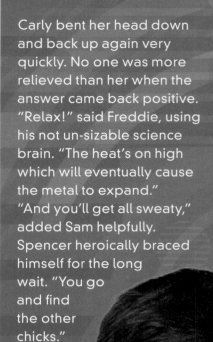

Duke decided to check out the room he loved the best – the kitchen. Freddie trailed after him just to make sure he didn't squash any little birdies by mistake. "Hey!" Freddie suddenly grinned. "I think I hear one behind the fridge!"

He pressed himself flat against the wall, then looked again. Yes, there was definitely a tiny ball of yellow fluff hiding behind the element! "Back up," said Duke calmly. "I'll move the fridge."

Freddie couldn't believe that it was possible. Spencer and Carly's fridge must have weighed at least a ton! "Move!" belted out Duke. "I love animals!" His science buddy quickly backed away from the fridge. Duke took a deep breath, gave the fridge a bear hug and then tried to raise it off the ground. Not surprisingly, he failed. Freddie was making a mental diagram involving a complex system of ropes and pulleys when Duke bent down to try again. "I always do better when Coach yells at me. You gotta do it if you want that baby chick to make it!" Freddie gulped. Screaming his head off at the biggest kid in school didn't come naturally to him, but he didn't have a lot of choice right now. "GO Lubberman go!" he bellowed. "You gotta want it! You gotta want it!" It was just the push Duke needed. Burning with testosterone and amped up to the max, he yelled a few times then grappled with the fridge. Freddie dived out the way as Duke body slammed the unit, sending it tumbling onto the floor. He couldn't bear to imagine what the neighbours would think. "Got him!" beamed Freddie, running into the corner and scooping up Omelette. Fred placed the chick back into the incubator, then ran over to where Spencer's legs were sticking out the ventilator shaft. "We got three of them!" explained Freddie. "Three more to go!" Spencer jiggled his legs appreciatively. "Thank you for keeping me in the loop."

75

iHatCh CHICKS

BACK up in the studio, the girls were hot on the trail of chick number four.
"I'm pretty sure that there's one up on that beam there," said Sam, pointing to the joist above her head. She craned her eyes to the ceiling. "Can we borrow a ladder from somebody in the building?"
Carly shook her head. This was a crisis situation!
"We don't have time," she muttered. "Lock your fingers together and boost me up!"
It was a struggle, but somehow they managed to hoist Carly up to the top.
"Come here chickie, chickie," coaxed Carly, crawling slowly forwards along the beam. Suddenly Carly let out a howl of pain.
"What happened?" asked Sam.
Carly sucked through her teeth.
"He pecked my finger!"

Sam turned away so that Carly wouldn't see her snigger. Unfortunately her BFF knew her evil mind far too well.
"Wipe that grin off your face!" she barked, not even bothering to look down. Sam straightened up and did as she was told.
"Try to grab him," she urged, watching the wall clock tick on through their out-of-incubator time.
"Wow, if only I'd thought of that," frowned Carly, getting seriously touchy. Somehow, she managed to crawl a little closer. She gently reached out an arm and put her hands around the tiny bird.

"He's almost in my…"
Suddenly Carly let out a shriek as the little bundle of fluff fluttered into the air.
"CATCH HIM!" begged Carly. Sam dived across the rug to make the type of goalie save that would have impressed David Beckham. She landed on her tummy with arms fully outstretched, just as the baby chick floated safely into her cupped palms.
"I got him!" grinned Sam, holding up her trophy. "Just be careful getting down from th…"
There was a little yelp as Carly tumbled off the beam and crashed onto the rug beside her.
"That," summed up Sam.
"Wasn't careful."

While Spencer kept his spirits up by singing a selection of tunes from the public domain, Freddie and Duke worked their way back round the living room.

"I hear peepin'," whispered Duke, running his hand along the wall. Freddie listened, then nodded. The wrestler was turning out to be quite an asset!

"There's a chick behind the plasterboard," confirmed Freddie, realising that he had no idea how to get it back out again.

"We gotta get in there," decided Duke.

Freddie started to pace anxiously up and down the room, turning over every option in his mind.

"My uncle's a carpenter," he reasoned. "Maybe he could bring over …"

At that moment, Duke let out a primal scream of glass-breaking proportions. Freddie squealed as the boy used his own head to butt a massive cavity in Carly's living room wall. He ducked behind the couch until the carnage was over. Duke's actions were instinctive, bestial, but highly effective. Freddie reached into the wall and reached out a healthy little chick. He blew the dust off its feathers then added the little guy to the incubator.

"What was that?" asked Spencer, his voice echoing out of the heating duct. Freddie tapped Spencer's feet reassuringly. "We found baby chick number four!"

"That's good," said Spencer bravely, trying not to break down. Before Duke could return to the mission, Freddie signalled for him to help pull on Spencer's feet. He figured that it must be getting pretty hot in the air vent now. The pair yanked and yanked until Spencer signalled that his hip bones were in danger of becoming estranged from their sockets.

"This isn't working," said Freddie, calling for a break. "Really?!" asked Spencer, his voice loaded with sarcasm. Freddie scratched his head. "I wish we could think of a way to smoothly slide him outta there." Duke suddenly made for the door like an over-sized puppy. "Did you say smoothie? I want one!" It wasn't a hard decision to let him go. "Tell them to add an intelligence boost!" Freddie called helpfully.

77

iHatch CHICKS

SAM and Carly ran down from the studio to deposit Yoko back in the incubator. "Only Poachy to go!" cheered Sam, introducing chick number five to her brothers and sisters. Carly ticked the chart, then turned seriously to Freddie. "How much longer do we have before bad things happen?" Freddie checked his phone. "About nine minutes!" "Ugh!" squeaked Carly, running up to the heating duct. "Spencer you OK in there?" "No!" boomed Spencer. Carly nodded, scanning the floorboards for feathers. "Well hang in there!" Sam followed Carly towards the elevator. "Freddie you keep looking down here, while we go back up!" By the time the girls had jumped into the lift, they were already down to eight minutes. "What if we don't find the little guy?" asked Sam, speaking the unspeakable. "Poor little Poachy," groaned Carly, wringing her hands. As soon as the lift reached the third floor, the friends hammered on the button that opened the door. It wasn't til they'd hurtled out into the studio, that they realised what they'd witnessed inside the lift. There, trapped behind the glass in the elevator window, was Poachy!

lol

The girls started to frantically prise the glass off the window, but it wouldn't budge. "Freddie, answer!" screamed Carly, bawling into the walkie talkie. Freddie radioed back straight away.
"There's a tool we can use in my tech trolley," he confirmed. "Comin' up straight away!" Everything would have been fine it he hadn't decided to use the lift.

Carly and Sam tore down the stairs at the same time as the elevator arrived. They pushed a confused Freddie out of the way and ran up to the window. "Why did you press that stupid button!" snapped Sam, as she peered through the glass. "What's goin' on?" gasped Freddie. "The last chick was behind that window," explained Carly. Or at least he had been.

Even though it wasn't his fault, Freddie was devastated. "He could be anywhere in the building by now," said Carly, checking her phone. "Anyway... it's too late." Nobody knew what to do or say. Freddie kicked a cushion across the floor, then sat down with his face in his hands. Carly sat down beside him. "We saved five of them," she whispered. "We woulda saved all six if I hadn't hit that button," frowned Freddie, swallowing down tears. "It wasn't your..." The rest of Carly's sentence was drowned out by the sound of muffled screams – Spencer! The gang ran over to the ventilation shaft. Spencer was making violent coughing noises while his legs twitched oddly at the same time! Sam quickly got a handle on the situation. "Uh-oh," she surmised. "He's freaking out!" "Let's try and pull him out of there again," shouted Freddie, grabbing a twitchy leg. "One, two, three!" yelled Carly. Somehow the threesome managed to heave the twenty-six-year-old out of the heating duct. All of them wound up sprawled across the floor with Spencer reduced to a wrecked, sweaty mess. "You all right?" asked Sam, dragging him to his feet. Spencer leant over the sofa and coughed a weird, echoey cough. Everybody winced as he carefully opened his mouth and spat a small, but perfectly-formed chick into his hands.

"You coughed up Poachy!" Freddie gushed with delight. Carly and Sam helped Spencer onto the couch, then danced around the living room. "It crawled into my mouth," Spencer explained, totally grossed out. "Worse thing was, it didn't even taste like chicken!"

BIRD BRAIN

How quickly could YOU find six cheeky chicks? Put your search and rescue skills to the test by tracing a path around Carly's apartment. Only one route through passes all six baby chickens – can you find it?

A   B   C

EXIT FRONT DOOR

ELEVATOR   BACK DOOR

THROW A CRAZY HAT PARTY

When iCarly became an overnight web hit, the team celebrated big style with a crazy hat party! Next time you've got something to smile about, try throwing one for all of your friends.

CARLY SAID THAT HER CRAZY HAT PARTY WAS A BLAST! EVEN FREDDIE'S SHY TECHY PALS FROM THE AV CLUB WERE BRAVE ENOUGH TO DRESS UP IN A SELECTION OF COMEDY CAPS. TRY IT NEXT BIRTHDAY – YES THAT IS AN ORDER!

IT'S A HAT... INVITATIONS

Fold a piece of card in half, then cut half a top hat shape out of the front to make cute fold-out invitations. Warn friends to bring a cool hat to the party – otherwise they'll be forced to take a lucky dip out of the host's hat stash.

CRAZY HAT GAMES

Party games are so much more fun when you work in a hat theme! Pass the hat, musical hats and pin the hat on the party host are just a handful of suggestions. We could go on…

HAT-TASTIC ART AND CRAFT

If you're an arty bunch cover a big table with newspaper and set out some art supplies. You'll need plenty of card, tape and decorations such as feathers and stick-on gems. Ask an adult to judge the hats and present the winner with a prize.

Top Crazy Hats

1. Bobble hat
2. Straw boater
3. Hard hat
4. Radio cap
5. Princess hat
6. Hats with woolly hair
7. Cowboy hat
8. Jester hat
9. Easter bonnet
10. Sombrero

FANTABULOUS
*BLOG!

Jake Krandle thinks that Carly and I are an ITEM!

SHOCK (AND ÜBER-GOOD) NEWS! The hottest boy in school actually believes that Carly and I are dating! BETTER news would be that Carly and I actually WERE dating, but you gotta take these things one step at a time.

It all started when Jake broke up with his girlfriend. While I battled to get past two meathead wrestlers that were having a fight in front of my locker, Carly was confessing her CRUSH to Sam. Instead of trying to put her off, Puckett irritatingly proceeded to get Carly talking to pretty boy right there and then!! That girl really is the PITS, but Carly likes her so what can you do?

I was totally BUMMED-OUT when Carly invited Jake round for a tour of the studio. Luckily, I got the chance to give the dude a good talking to in the hall – if some other guy was going to spend time with my Carly I needed to make pretty damn sure that his intentions were honourable!

Later when I was having tea with my mum, Carly txted me asking if I'd come up and do a sound check. I nearly dropped the phone into my eggs and soldiers (Sam – shut up) when she told me that she'd asked Jake to perform a song live on the show!

The next night Jake was strumming his guitar and doing something that was meant to sound like singing. I say meant to, 'cos he was totally RUBBISH! Even Carly would have cut him out of the show if he hadn't explained that his grandma was logging in especially to hear her little Jakey sing. Being a sweet-hearted girl, Carly fell for his sob story HOOK, LINE and SINKER. Being a heartless control-freak with a fondness for inflicting pain, Sam didn't.

No matter, they both agreed that I should use some of my audio software to make Jake's voice sound in-tune for the performance. I eventually agreed (it was the Chinese burn from Sam that did it), and it was SO WORTH IT!! Afterwards the lovely Miss Shay gave me a nose kiss to say thank you, and NOBODY forced her to do it! It's a moment that I'll never forget, EVER!

The next day things got better and better. After his knock-out performance on the show Jake got back together with his old girlfriend. He also told Carly that he felt weird about getting in between HER AND ME! She wasn't best pleased, but I was PSYCHED!! Now that Jake's spoken for, maybe she'll realise that she and I are just MEANT TO BE!

Freddie

Sam here. All I can say is don't hold ya breath.

Sam again. That ain't gonna change anytime soon geek-boy! TTFN.

STARRING...

IN THIS SEQUENCE FROM THE FIRST-EVER EPISODE, CARLY AND SAM ARE IN A STATE OF PANIC. FREDDIE HAS UPLOADED THEIR PRIVATE CONVERSATION ONTO THE WORLD WIDE WEB! ONCE MISS BRIGGS HEARS THEIR COMMENTS ABOUT HER POINTY BOOBS, THEY'RE BOUND TO LAND IN SERIOUS TROUBLE...

CAST — □ X

 Carly Shay

 Sam Puckett

 Freddie Benson

Go

EPISODE 101: IPILOT

Act 2, Sc 1 – Carly and Spencer's apartment, late at night.

[Sam is jumping up and down in panic, as Carly frantically hits the keys on her laptop.]

SAM: Can you remove it?!

CARLY: [trying] Maybe... [Gets frustrated] Ullchh! I need Freddie's password!

SAM: Which apartment does he live in?

CARLY: The one across the hall. But it's after midnight so you probably shouldn't...

[Sam runs out of the door. Carly keeps working on the computer.]

CARLY (CONT'D): Oh, great. Now twenty-eight thousand people have watched us!

[We hear Freddie scream offstage, then Carly turns to see Sam dragging the boy in by his foot. Poor Freddie is sliding on his back across the floor, squealing in pain.]

FREDDIE: Quit it, Sam! Let go of my foot! Too much friction! Let go!

[Sam lets go. Freddie quickly scrambles to his feet.]

FREDDIE (CONT'D): [to Sam] What is the matter with you?!

CARLY: Why'd you film us at the auditions today?

FREDDIE: Oh 'cos you guys were being funny.

SAM: Well, you shouldn't have put us on-line without our permission!

FREDDIE: I didn't! I edited you guys out before I uploaded the auditions.

CARLY: No, you did the opposite of that!

FREDDIE: What?! [Freddie gets on the computer] There's no way I... [he sees it's true] Uh-oh.

SAM: Yeah.

CARLY: Just take us off the site!

FREDDIE: OK, OK! Just gimme a sec...

[Freddie clicks the mouse and types as fast as he can.]

CARLY: [pacing up and down] Ohhhh, this is so not good. [Turning to Sam] Anyone... anyone in the world can just click and see everything we did and said today.

SAM: It's so embarrassing. And if Miss Briggs sees...

CARLY: Don't even talk about it. 'Cos if she...

FREDDIE: Ha! Got it. (Reads from the computer screen) See, it says, 'At your request, this video will be removed.'

CARLY/SAM: Good! / Finally.

FREDDIE: ...Tomorrow morning.

CARLY/SAM: [upset] Aw, man! / Freddie!

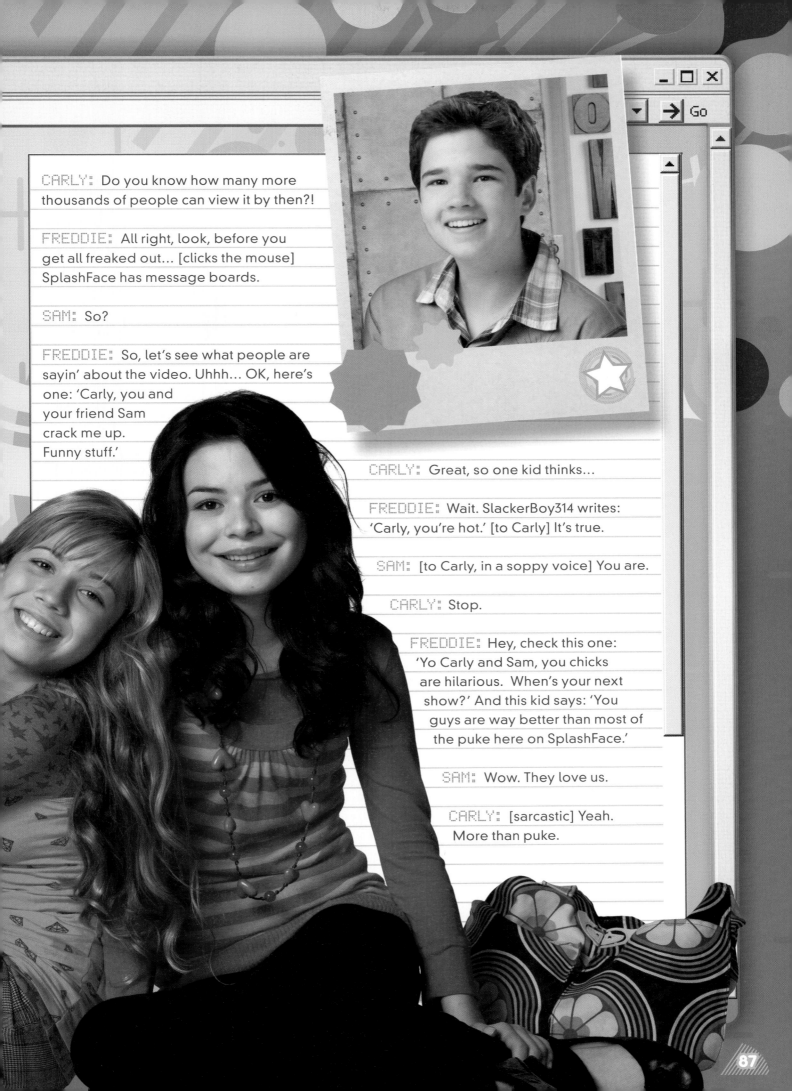

CARLY: Do you know how many more thousands of people can view it by then?!

FREDDIE: All right, look, before you get all freaked out… [clicks the mouse] SplashFace has message boards.

SAM: So?

FREDDIE: So, let's see what people are sayin' about the video. Uhhh… OK, here's one: 'Carly, you and your friend Sam crack me up. Funny stuff.'

CARLY: Great, so one kid thinks…

FREDDIE: Wait. SlackerBoy314 writes: 'Carly, you're hot.' [to Carly] It's true.

SAM: [to Carly, in a soppy voice] You are.

CARLY: Stop.

FREDDIE: Hey, check this one: 'Yo Carly and Sam, you chicks are hilarious. When's your next show?' And this kid says: 'You guys are way better than most of the puke here on SplashFace.'

SAM: Wow. They love us.

CARLY: [sarcastic] Yeah. More than puke.

iWant to DATE FREDDIE

SAM and Carly thrashed electric guitars, jumping about the apartment like loons moshing to the beat. Freddie tried to keep up with the pair as they staggered around in front of the camera. Sometimes the girls ducked out of shot, but he was pretty sure that viewers were getting the gist. Sam decided to round things up. "And that totally proves…"

"…that neither me nor Sam can play the guitar," chipped in Carly, tossing her guitar out of frame. It was time for a brand new segment.

"Bring on the Blab Cam!" shouted Sam and Carly at the same time. Freddie stopped shooting so that he could correct them. "Actually it's called two-way high-speed video conferencing…"

"Freddie," smiled Carly. "Can we just talk to someone?" After a random interview with a Polish guy, a pretty girl from Seattle came on the screen.

"My name's Valerie," she began. "Long-time viewer, first-time Blab Cammer. I just love iCarly."

"Haven't we seen you before?" asked Sam, taking a closer look at the monitor.

The girl blushed. "I'm in the year above at Ridgeway. Is Freddie there? Can I see him?" Freddie grinned and hit a button on his hip. The show switched to B-Cam, allowing him to give Valerie a wave. "Can I just say that I think that you're insanely cute?" gushed Valerie. Sam twirled her finger in the air. "You might wanna check your webcam and your brain cos one of them's malfunctioning." Despite Sam's misgivings, Valerie was serious. Freddie found himself being asked for a date live on air! Once he established that Carly could handle the jealousy, he accepted the offer before the girl changed her mind.

After the show, Freddie and the gang tucked into some melon. Even though Sam was ribbing him like crazy, it felt pretty good to have a first date lined up. Suddenly the buzzer went and his mum popped over from across the hall.

"I can't believe that it's finally happening!" cooed Mrs Benson, carrying a freshly pressed pile of smart 'date' clothes. "We're all in shock," nodded Sam solemnly. Freddie shrugged. "I'm not even sure if I'm going yet." "There is a living breathing girl out there who wants to go out with you," roared his mother. "This may never happen again, unless Carly changes her mind." Carly tried to be kind. "Freddie and I are just buds." Mrs Benson nodded sympathetically, before completely breaking down. "Why won't you love my son?" A quick scowl from Freddie and his mum recovered herself. She told the guys how she had the whole date planned out. "I'll cook dinner, then we're going to look at your baby pictures," she nodded proudly, turning to Sam. "Freddie had the cutest little bottom." Sam chuckled. "I'll give you a thousand dollars for a photo of Freddie's butt." Carly couldn't stand Freddie's pain any longer. "Mrs Benson?" she said gently. "We already told Freddie that he could have his date here." "Her brother's an amazing cook," added Freddie, desperate to persuade his mum to butt out. Mrs Benson finally agreed. Valerie was in for one heck of a treat. A date with techno-whiz Freddie AND Spencer's spaghetti tacos.

iWant to DATE FREDDIE

THE next night, Carly and Sam whizzed round the apartment getting everything perfect for the big date. The table was set, there were flowers dotted round the place and Spencer's spaghetti tacos were smelling great. Suddenly Freddie burst in wearing the lamest shirt and tank top his friends had ever seen. "Mum, will ya stop it?" he yelled, as Mrs Benson followed him around carrying a hairdryer. "But I'm not done fluffing your hair!" she protested. "Yes," answered Freddie desperately. "You are." The poor first-dater bundled his mum into the hallway and slammed the door shut. Then he set the latch chain and pulled the bolt across for good measure. Sam eyed him up and down, chuckling to herself.

"What's up with the outfit?" Freddie explained that his mum had dragged him out shopping, before asking Carly to fetch his back-up gear. While the girls were out of the room, he decided to ask Spencer for some man-to-man dating advice. "Just stare into her eyes and say nothing," replied Carly's big bro. "It'll make you look cool and mysterious." Freddie almost fell for the stare-into-their-eyes approach, until he remembered that Spencer hadn't had a girlfriend in ages. At that moment, Carly and Sam bowled back down the stairs. "Got your clothes," said Carly, handing him a T-shirt.

Before Freddie could change something terrible happened – Valerie rang the doorbell! There was total panic. During the chaos Sam opened the door then slammed it again in the girl's face. It wasn't a great move, but she figured that her stalling technique was better than letting Valerie see Freddie's stupid clothes.

After a shaky start, Freddie and Valerie's date seemed to be going surprisingly well. Carly and Sam were pretty sure of this, because they were watching the whole thing on the upstairs webcam. "We are bad people," muttered Carly, not taking her eyes off the screen. Sam smirked proudly and got comfy on her beanbag. It promised to be a long, but entertaining night...

Downstairs, Spencer waited table while Freddie and Valerie got to know each other a little better. "This is a really good spaghetti taco," said Freddie, smiling at his date. Valerie nodded, while Spencer cleared the plates. Upstairs Sam and Carly cringed as Freddie rattled off a string of unforgivable geek gags. Weirdly, Valerie seemed to be lapping it up. "I've never met someone who's so funny and knows so much about audio and video," she cooed appreciatively. Freddie was on a roll. "Hey," he joked. "Nobody knows audio and video like Freddie-o." Valerie laughed at just the right moment. "Anyway Freddie, who helps you with all the technical stuff on iCarly?" Freddie beamed proudly. "It's all me." "Amazing," gushed Valerie. "It looks so cool online." Freddie smiled modestly. Could this date get any better?

¡Want to DATE FREDDIE

A few days' later in school, Sam and Carly demanded a full date-update. "We've gone out together every night this week so far," grinned Freddie. "I'd say we're almost officially boyfriend and girlfriend." Sam scratched her head. "So which one are you?" Carly was just about to probe into what kissing action Freddie had seen when his mate Jeremy walked down the hall. Before he could even say hello, Jeremy sneezed violently into an over-sized hankie. "Still got that cold?" asked Carly wearily. Everyone knew that the poor guy had had a cold since forever. "Yeah," nodded Jeremy. "You comin' to that computer expo this weekend Freddie?" Freddie shook his head. "Nah, I'm going roller skating with Valerie."

Jeremy replied with a huge, conversation-busting `A-TISH-OO!` Knowing that he couldn't find a line to follow that display, the kid hurried off to class. "Man," giggled Sam. "I don't think I've ever seen that boy when he wasn't sneezing and..." She turned round and gawped at the empty hall behind her. Freddie had vamoosed! "Wasn't there a dork standing next to me a minute ago?" asked Sam, looking over her shoulder. Carly nodded then pointed towards the lockers. There was Freddie, helping Valerie fetch down her science folder. Looked like this dating business was working out rather well all round...

REC ●

Freddie beamed. Valerie was looking cuter than ever today! "Just been thinkin' about our first date," she grinned. "Remember how you told me what fun it was doing a webcast?" Freddie nodded and stepped a little closer – this chick was sooo into him! "I really wanna do one too," added Valerie. "Will you help me tomorrow night? I know nothing about all that techie stuff." Her new squeeze sighed. "Tomorrow night's when I do iCarly. I'll help you any other one though." Valerie's face fell. "No thanks. I really want to do it tomorrow." "But Carly and Sam are my friends," stuttered Freddie, his heart sinking. "I can't just bail on them."

That was exactly what Valerie wanted him to do. She looked at him with big doe eyes that Freddie found had to resist. "Sam doesn't sound like a friend to me," she whispered gently. "Doesn't she always call you names and tell you how you're not important to the show." "She can't help it! She's just naturally vicious," argued Freddie, unable to believe that he was actually awake and standing up for Sam. "Whatever," frowned Valerie, dismissing him with one hand. "I'll just find someone else to help me." Freddie's heart sank as she started to walk down the hall – how could he be so dumb as to lose his girlfriend after just four days? "Wait!" he yelled, suddenly making a decision. "I guess Carly and Sam can find another tech producer." Valerie turned on her heel, her face lighting up. She tripped back to Freddie and planted a delighted kiss on his lips. "Awwww, now that's my Freddie Bear."

iWant to
DATE FREDDIE

CARLY paced up and down in front of her couch – where was her BFF when she needed her? After ten more agonising minutes, Sam finally knocked on the front door.

"Hey I got your text message…" she smiled, before Carly yanked her in by her shirt.

"Freddie quit," bawled Carly, slamming the door behind her. "By email."

"He can't quit," gasped Sam. "Let's go and slap some sense into that boy!" It was the reaction Carly had been waiting for. There was no way the little punk was going to be able to desert the greatest web show on the planet! The friends stormed out of the apartment and across the hall. After pounding on the door and shouting like madwomen, Sam got impatient.

"What are you doin'?" asked Carly.

Sam held up a hairpin. "Picking the lock." With Sam's criminal skills the pair were inside in seconds. Carly watched through her fingers as Sam found Freddie's hiding place then dragged him squealing back across the hall.

"That was assault!" shrieked Freddie, but this was no time for pleasantries.

"Why are you quitting iCarly?" demanded Carly.

"Because I don't like the way that Sam treats me," answered Freddie. "She's always mean to me. Even if I get an ice cream cone she always takes it and licks it just to bug me!"

"Great!" dismissed Carly. "Now what's the real reason?" It was time to tell the truth.

"Valerie wants to do a web show with me as tech producer," muttered Freddie, staring at the floorboards.

Sam was disgusted. "You'd ditch us for a show that's competing against us?" she spat. "Dump the chick now!"

Freddie felt his cheeks go red. "You were the guys that talked me into goin' out with her in the first place!"

Sam was about to jump back in, when Carly put her hand up.

"Stop," she said quietly to Sam. "He should help his girlfriend."

The next night, Sam and Carly got ready to shoot their latest episode of iCarly. Luckily Freddie hadn't left them totally high and dry – he'd found a replacement tech producer to take over. The unlucky part was that it had turned out to be Jeremy. "Five... four... AT–CHOO! "he blustered, unable to get through the countdown without a rip-roaring sneeze. 'Let's just go!' urged Carly, kicking off the show. Sam turned to the camera that was shaking more with every sneeze. "We'd like to welcome aboard a new member of the team. Meet Jeremy…" The budding tech producer turned the camcorder round to face himself, before hacking all over the lens. Jeremy's camera work had been pretty ropey, but this was too gross for words.

"I got some spittle on the glass," he whispered awkwardly. Sam couldn't bear to look. "Just wipe it off Jeremy," sighed Carly.
As the team limped through the show, Carly moved onto a new segment called 'Animals Dressed Like Other Animals'.

"First up we have a dog dressed like a pig!" said Sam, as Carly led a cute sausage dog onto the set. The little thing stared blankly at the camera, probably wondering why it was wearing a pink snout and a hair band with little piggy ears stuck on to it. As Sam explained that their friend Robin had lent the dog to the show, Jeremy's nose started to twitch alarmingly. "Uh, I'm allergic to pigs," he stuttered.
Carly thought that she was going to scream. "It's not a pig, it's a dog!" It was no good. Jeremy needed a tissue.
"Okay!" grinned Carly through gritted teeth. "We're gonna wrap up the show a little early tonight." Sam stared daggers at the hapless producer as he rattled out a volley of sneezes. "So join us next week at iCarly.com." Carly grimaced. "Maybe."

¡Want to DATE FREDDIE

JEREMY'S germ-infested episode put Sam in a stinking mood for days. When Valerie accosted her in the school hall, she was treated to a suitably chilly reception. "I watched iCarly the other night," said Freddie's girlfriend, making an irritating 'ick' face. Sam gave it right back. "I don't need your review, right?" Valerie looked hurt. "Don't be mad at me."

"I will be mad at you!" shouted Sam. "You stole Freddie and that hurt our show." Valerie pulled her to one side and whispered in her ear. "You don't need iCarly." Sam's eyes popped, but she let her rival continue. "Come do my show with me," she smiled archly. "I mean, c'mon. iCarly's gonna crash and burn without Freddie." "Y'know that Carly happens to be my friend," replied Sam, her fingers tingling with rage. Valerie pouted innocently. "Then why isn't your web show called 'Carly and Sam'? If you were my co-host I'd call it 'Val and Sam'. Or maybe even 'Sam and Val.'" Sam scowled, then stopped for a minute. Although she was sorely tempted to give the object of Freddie's affection a good hiding, she decided to play her at her own game.

"This is a serious offer?" she asked, pretending to think about it. "You, me and Freddie." Valerie nodded. "We'll knock Carly Shay right off the internet. That's been my plan all along." "You've got a devious little brain," complimented Sam. "I like that." Val smirked, sure she'd hit a winner. "Let's talk tomorrow." Sam flashed an insincere smile back at her wannabe partner-in-crime. "Absolutely."

As they parted, Valerie scanned the corridor, making out she was looking for someone. "Don't say anything will you? We don't want Carly to know about this."

Sam scooted round to Carly's loft in two seconds flat. Once she'd spilled the whole sorry story, Carly's response was just as expected.

"That little…" Carly tried to check herself, but this was too much. "SKUNK BAG!" Suddenly Valerie and Freddie's luvved-up dates didn't seem quite so cosy. "Oh my god!" she screeched. "She's using Freddie."

"Yeah and now she wants to use me too!" spluttered Sam. Freddie needed to be confronted right away. "You're talking about my girlfriend!" he shouted defensively after Carly and Sam had marched across the hall.

"She's not your girlfriend," pressed Carly. "She's just using you." The comment hurt, but Freddie wasn't going to give up on his new dating status that easily. "I enjoy being used!" Sam stepped in and shook him by the collar. "She tried to get me to be on her webshow too." Freddie argued that Sam was lying, but Carly wasn't going to let him cop out that easily. "Sam may be obnoxious and rude, but she doesn't lie!" she blasted, turning to her best friend with a quick, "You know I love you."

"Fine!" exploded Freddie. "I'll go ask Valerie myself."

"She's not gonna tell you the truth!" flashed Sam, hitting her own head with a loud, "duh!"

"She's using you," repeated Carly. iCarly's ex-tech producer grabbed his coat.

"Believe us!" yelled Sam. "We've been your friends way longer than she has!" Too late. Freddie had already stormed down the stairs.

¡iWant to
DATE FREDDIE

CARLY was totally depressed. She didn't think that she could face another webcast with Jeremy, but with five minutes to go 'til the next episode of iCarly she didn't have a lot of choice. She could just imagine Valerie snuggling up to her old friend Freddie then settling down gleefully to watch the show. "Where's Germy?" she asked an equally bummed-out Sam. "In the bathroom," muttered Sam. "He brought special nose plugs that are supposed to keep snot from dripping out of his nostrils."
Carly nodded grimly. "Charming."

Just then, Jeremy stomped in with two bean-shaped tubes of plastic wedged up his nose. "These plugs should keep me from…" the tech-producer spluttered then sneezed with such intensity his right nose plug flew out of his nostril like a green and rather slimy torpedo. "Uugh!!"
Sam decided that she was going to have to kill Jeremy. As she pulled the sticky plug off her cheek, she shot him a look of such disgust the poor kid ran and sneezed his way straight out of the apartment.

"Now what?" asked Carly. "We can't do the show without someone doing the techy stuff." Just at that moment, the lift doors opened with a PING! Freddie stepped sadly into the room. "You guys were right," he said. "Valerie is a skunk bag." Explaining that he had broken up with her on the spot, Freddie absentmindedly reset some of the keys on Jeremy's laptop. Suddenly Sam remembered that they were due to go on air any second. "Come on!" she grinned. "Let's do a butt-kicking webshow to take your mind off it!" But Freddie wasn't ready to come back on the team quite yet. "Valerie wasn't wrong when she said that you guys don't treat me like I'm important to the show." Carly started to defend herself, but Freddie was too busy staring out Sam. After a lot of soul-searching and a kick in the ribs from her best friend, Sam walked over and gave him a hug. "OK," she said seriously. "You're just as important to the show as we are." Freddie was back like a shot. It was a very special, intimate moment – until Sam drew it to a close by grabbing his boxers and giving him a wedgie.

"You guys rocked tonight!" buzzed Spencer, as the gang sat down for some post-show melon. Freddie smiled proudly.

"I'm back on iCarly…"

"…as our permanent technical producer," added Carly, beaming. Sam suddenly got a devilish look in her eye. "So what's Valerie gonna do about her show?"

Freddie flipped open his laptop and punched some words into Splashface. Within seconds, Valerie's site was up. The friends gathered round to enjoy her latest webcast SANS Freddie.

"Er, if you'll just take a look at the monitor above me," she stammered. "You'll see a video of my family's recent trip to Idaho, the home of the potato.

Sam rolled her eyes. She expected it to be lame, but not this lame! On the laptop, Valerie fumbled about with three remote controls. Not one of them appeared to be working.

"Why won't it play?" she blasted. After pressing numerous buttons, Valerie got impatient. She whacked the flat screen with such force it fell off its fittings, taking her out her with it.

"Is she OK?" gasped Carly, trying not to smile.

Sam casually pointed back to the computer screen.

"Yeah, she's getting up."

A crazy bed-hair version of Valerie hoisted herself back into the frame. The show was turning out to be comedy gold, but for some reason she didn't seem to see the joke. Instead Valerie turned back to the screen and shrugged.

"I don't know what to do now?" she bleated desperately.

"I do!" grinned Freddie, clicking the browser window shut.

The gang burst into giggles. It was definitely time for more melon.

IT SHOULDN'T HAPPEN
to Lewbert

SAM DOESN'T WAKE UP AND DELIBERATELY SET OUT TO TORMENT CARLY'S DOORMAN, HE JUST BRINGS THE DARK SIDE OUT IN HER! SPENCER TRIES TO KEEP THE KIDS UNDER CONTROL, BUT EVEN HE AGREES THAT THAT MEAN-FACED MAN DESERVES TO BE PRANKED EVERY NOW AND THEN. HERE IS A SELECTION OF THE BEST...

APRIL FOOLS

This one totally freaked Lewbert out! Every time Sam entered Bushwell Plaza, she would warn the doorman that April Fools was comin' soon. She even developed a cruel knowing cackle that would send him scuttling away with his fingers in his ears! By the time the big day arrived his nerves were so shot, she only had to look at him to provoke a hysterical reaction. Lewbert spent most of the afternoon checking his desk for booby traps...

FIZZY POP

Spencer couldn't resist this one. After Lewbert had been particularly obnoxious to the old lady on the 13th floor, Spence cruised into the lobby and offered him a bottle of cola. While Lewbert wasn't looking, he dropped a couple of sugar-coated pieces of chocolate into the top of the bottle. Next time Lewbert slurped —erk! – cola foamed everywhere!

UPSIDE DOWN DESK

One rainy Sunday, the iCarly team were bored when inspiration struck! Knowing it was Lewbert's afternoon off, they crept into the lobby and turned everything on his desk upside down. Photos, keyboard, books and the waste basket all went Australian. You should have seen his face when he opened his diary on the last page and thought it was Christmas!

FILL IN THE BLANKS

SOMEONE SNEAKY HAS CREPT INTO THE APARTMENT AND ATTACKED CARLY'S NOTEBOOK WITH A BOTTLE OF CORRECTION FLUID! USE YOUR KNOWLEDGE OF CARLY'S WORLD TO WRITE OVER THE BLANKS WITH A BRIGHT FELT-TIP PEN.

1. Carly's father works on a _____.
2. Freddie is totally besotted with _____.
3. Spencer's grandad wanted him to train as a _____.
4. At school, Sam usually gets a couple of _____ a week.
5. Freddie's overbearing mum is called _____.
6. The iCarly team once tried to break a record for the longest continuous _____.
7. When iCarly became a hit, the gang threw a crazy _____ party.
8. iCarly's harshest critic is called _____.
9. _____ Krandle is the hottest boy at Ridgeway High.
10. Freddie's official role is permanent tech-_____.

☐ MRS BENSON   ☐ NEVEL
☐ PRODUCER   ☐ DETENTIONS
☐ WEBCAST   ☐ CARLY
☐ LAWYER   ☐ SUBMARINE
☐ JAKE   ☐ HAT

COOL CLIPS

Here's a special place for you to record all the best clips from the web! Draw pictures of the posts on iCarly and other sites that got you laughing or left you wanting to see more.

FUNNIEST CLIP

GROSSEST WEBPOST

MOST
UNFORGETTABLE
POST

MOST SHOCHING
CLIP

BIGGEST TALENT
ON THE WEB

TOP ICARLY
MOMENT

Pimp Your SCREEN!

COMPUTER SCREENS NEED NEVER BE BORING AGAIN! FREDDIE AND CARLY USE ART SUPPLIES AND CRAFT FOAM TO GIVE THEIR COMPUTERS A LOOK TO MATCH THEIR MOOD. CARLY'S PIMPED HERS WITH A BRIGHT PINK FRAME AND GLOW-IN-THE-DARK STARS. FREDDIE'S DECORATED HIS SO THAT IT MATCHES HIS SCREENSAVER. YEP, YOU GUESSED, THE MONITOR'S COVERED WITH PICS OF CARLY!

TO DECORATE YOUR PC, YOU WILL NEED:

Long ruler
Pencil
Notepad
Large sheet of craft foam
Old newspaper
PVA glue
Photos, magazine cuttings, glitter, stickers, gems and fabric paint to decorate
Blu-Tack

1. Use a ruler to measure the outside of your computer monitor, then jot the dimensions down. Next measure the interior screen size.

2. Find a sheet of craft foam in your favourite colour and then cut out an even rectangle as large as the measurements of the outside of the monitor.

3. Now hold the piece of foam up to the monitor and lightly mark with a pencil where the four corners of the screen area are placed.

4. Put the foam back on the table and draw lines between the four points, using your measurements of the interior screen size to keep the rectangle accurate. Carefully cut the screen outline out of the foam. Now you have a frame!

5. Lay your frame on some newspaper and start decorating. Glue on photos of your fave stars, friends and add glitter if you want to. Stickers, gems and craft foam shapes also work well. Draw designs in fabric paint too.

6. Use Blu-Tack to put your frame in place. Enjoy!

+++ ASK AN ADULT BEFORE FIXING STUFF ON YOUR SCREEN. GET THEIR HELP WHEN CUTTING OUT WITH SHARP SCISSORS TOO. +++

You're LIVE!

WORKING ON iCARLY IS THE COOLEST THING EVER! THE HILARIOUS CLIPS JUST KEEP GETTING BETTER AND BETTER, AND THE REASON FOR THAT IS YOU!

If you'd like to send a video in to the show, visit icarly.com to find out what to do. Here's a few tips in the meantime to make sure that your tape is as awesome as it can be...

1. STAND CLOSE TO THE CAMERA, BUT NOT SO CLOSE THAT WE CAN SEE YOUR NOSE HAIRS, JUST CLOSE ENOUGH THAT WE CAN SEE YOUR FACE!

2. SAY YOUR FIRST NAME AND YOUR AGE, THEN STEP BACK AND DO YOUR THING!

3. REMEMBER, THE CLOSER YOU ARE TO THE CAMERA, THE BETTER WE'LL HEAR YOUR VOICE!

4. MAKE SURE YOUR CLOTHES DON'T HAVE LOGOS OR BAD WORDS ON THEM.

5. DON'T SAY OR SHOW FULL NAMES, SCHOOL NAMES, CITIES, STREET NAMES, PHONE NUMBERS, OR EMAIL ADDRESSES IN YOUR VIDEO.

6. TRY TO KEEP YOUR VIDEO SHORTER THAN THREE MINUTES.

7. DON'T DO ANYTHING DANGEROUS. YOU DON'T WANT TO GET HURT!

8. ALWAYS MAKE AND KEEP YOUR OWN BACKUP OF YOUR VIDEO. WE CAN'T SEND YOUR VIDEO BACK TO YOU. SO, MAKE AND KEEP A COPY FOR YOURSELF!

GOOD LUCK, WE CAN'T WAIT TO SEE IT*!

*(Note from Sam) Apart from the guy that bathed in a tub of scrambled egg, that was just GROSS! No more submissions from you, thank you very much!

RECORD SMASHING BLOG!

My sculpture made the history books!

BFF

GREETINGS ICARLITES! FORGIVE ME if I don't sound my usual bubbly, charming self – I didn't get many ZZZs during the last couple of days. In fact, I didn't get ANY!! Me and the iCarly team were up all hours trying to break the record for the 'World's Longest Webcast'.

Techmeister Fredward made sure that the attempt was 100% official. To get in the book, Carly and Sam had to be on air for 24 hours and 8 minutes. That's one heck of a lot of RANDOM DANCING! The guys from Jonas even sent over a hot babe called Marilyn to make sure that the webcast followed all the rules.

While the guys started the show, I had a great time working on my latest sculpture and hanging with Marilyn. My latest piece of art was fitted out with 137 working parts, neat huh? Some people try and say that my creations are made out of old junk, but I prefer to say that I work with vintage materials.

When I bolted the last section in place on my sculpture, Marilyn